Science

Environmental Science
LANDFORMS and CYCLES

Oceanic crust - destruction
1.4.?

Block **4**

Cover image The Ship Rock, northwestern New Mexico.

The Open University, Walton Hall, Milton Keynes, MK7 6AA

First published 2002, Reprinted 2006.

Edited, designed and typeset by The Open University.

Printed and bound at the University Press, Cambridge.

ISBN 0 7492 6990 1

This publication forms part of an Open University course, S216 *Environmental Science*. Details of this and other Open University courses can be obtained from the Course Information and Advice Centre, PO Box 724, The Open University, Milton Keynes MK7 6ZS, United Kingdom: tel. +44 (0)1908 653231, e-mail ces-gen@open.ac.uk

Alternatively, you may visit the Open University website at http://www.open.ac.uk where you can learn more about the wide range of courses and packs offered at all levels by The Open University.

To purchase this publication or other components of Open University courses, contact Open University Worldwide Ltd, The Open University, Walton Hall, Milton Keynes MK7 6AA, United Kingdom: tel. +44 (0)1908 858785; fax +44 (0)1908 858787; e-mail ouwenq@open.ac.uk; website http://www.ouw.co.uk

2.1

s216 block 4i2.1

PART 1

LANDFORMS

Mark Sephton and Sandy Smith

Plate tectonics

1

This block of the course is about landforms — the physical features of the Earth's land surface, where they occur, how they form and how they change. 'Landscape' is a term that is sometimes used instead of 'landform' but has a different meaning, as it includes the modification of landforms by plants and animals, including human activity: it is what you see when you look around you. In this block we will investigate landforms, not landscapes.

The development and evolution of landforms involves processes in the solid Earth (the **geosphere**), the atmosphere, the hydrosphere and the biosphere, which interact with each other. This section looks at relevant processes in the geosphere; later sections will bring in the modification of the geosphere by atmospheric, hydrospheric and biospheric processes.

range of environments that support living organisms

1.1 The surface of the Earth

The primary division of the Earth's surface is straightforward, into land and oceans with the oceans covering 71% of the surface. This gives the Earth a unique appearance in the solar system (from space it is a blue planet, Figure 1.1). Large-scale features are shown in more detail on the poster 'The Earth's surface'. Before continuing with this section you need to spread out the poster on a table in front of you, or have it pinned to a wall next to where you are sitting. An atlas, if you have one, may also be helpful to name specific features.

Figure 1.1 The Earth from space, with Australia, parts of Asia and the Indian and Pacific Oceans. Taken by a weather satellite in December 1997.

The poster shows the shape of the Earth's solid surface as if the oceans had been drained. Green, yellow, reddish-brown and grey shades indicate progressively higher land, and deepening shades of blue indicate increasing depth of the ocean floor. Probably the most familiar features are the coastal outlines of the landmasses and the major mountain belts such as the Alps in Europe and the Himalayas in Asia. To help you to appreciate the shape of the Earth's undulating surface, the map is shaded as if illuminated from the left-hand side of the poster. This means that surfaces that slope down to the west are lit and appear bright, whereas eastward facing slopes are 'in shadow' and appear dark. This applies both over the land areas and on the ocean floor. Thus, the ocean floor slopes down to the west off the western coast of Africa, showing up as a white, illuminated, band. The eastern side, however, appears dark and in shadow even though the depths are the same as on the west side.

○ Does the poster show the entire area of the Earth?

● No. The latitudes beyond 75° N and 75° S have been left off, as can be seen from the labelled latitude scale on the left and right-hand edges of the poster.

Our reason for neglecting the polar regions stems from the difficulty of representing on a flat surface the true shapes and relative sizes of every geographical feature that lies on a sphere. On the poster map, all lines of latitude have the same length as the Equator (so that the map has a rectangular shape) whereas in reality lines of latitude get shorter and shorter as the poles are approached. The effect of this is to make areas far from the Equator look unrealistically large. Very close to the poles the distortion is so large as to make the map almost meaningless, which is why the polar regions have been cropped from the poster.

Now let's use the poster map to investigate the Earth. Why do we see what we see? The poster map shows a considerable amount of detail, so it makes sense to concentrate on particular parts rather than try to deal with everything at once. We'll start with the land surface.

1.1.1 Mountain belts

The mountainous regions of the Earth are notable features of the land. On the poster, shades of reddish-brown are used to identify places of more than about 2000 m elevation above sea-level. Many of these regions are linear features, extending over many thousands of kilometres; they are known as **mountain belts**. Dramatic examples occur along the western side of North America (the Rocky Mountains), the western side of South America (the Andes), and there is a chain running east from the European Alps, through the Middle East and the Himalayas. The Earth's highest point is the summit of the Himalayan peak Mount Everest, which is 8848 m above sea-level (Figure 1.2). In northwest Africa, along the coast, lies another mountain belt — the Atlas Mountains. Slightly lower mountain belts are found along the east coast of the USA (the Appalachians), across Norway and Sweden, and running north–south in central Russia (the Urals).

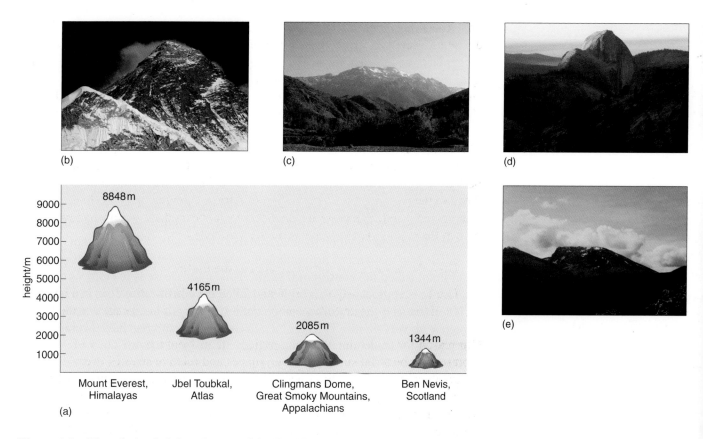

Figure 1.2 The relative heights of some of the Earth's mountains. (a) The heights of major peaks in various mountain belts; (b) Mount Everest, Himalayas, Asia; (c) Jbel Toubkal, Atlas Mountains, northwest Africa; (d) Clingmans Dome, Great Smoky Mountains, eastern USA; and (e) Ben Nevis, Scotland.

○ Is there a pattern of where mountain belts occur on continents? Are they generally in the middle or on the edges?

● Many mountain belts lie at or near the edge of continents as in North and South America and southern Europe. However, there are significant mountain belts within continents, such as the Himalayas and the Urals.

1.1.2 The ocean floor

It may initially seem odd, in a block on landforms, to look at the ocean floor. However, the geospheric process that has the main effect on landforms involves the shape of the ocean floor as well as the land surface, so we will look at the ocean floor as well as the land.

Around each continent is a region that on the poster is shaded in pale blue. This is the **continental shelf**, where the ocean floor lies no more than 200 m below the ocean's surface.

○ How variable is the width of the continental shelf?

● The width of the continental shelf varies considerably. For example, it is much narrower around Africa than it is around the British Isles, where the North Sea is part of the continental shelf.

Question 1.1

Consider a voyage across the Atlantic Ocean from the British Isles to North America. In three or four sentences, describe in qualitative terms (i.e. numerical values of depth are not required) how the ocean depth changes with distance as you travel westwards.

An alternative, pictorial, way of describing the shape of the ocean floor is to draw a cross-section through the Earth. Such a diagram shows the undulations of the Earth's surface along a line between two places on the surface.

Figure 1.3 shows the specific example of a cross-section between the eastern Pacific Ocean and western Africa, along a roughly west–east line that crosses South America and the South Atlantic Ocean. The continental shelf on the west coast of Africa is labelled on the extreme right-hand side of this diagram. Immediately to the west of the continental shelf lies a much steeper part of the ocean floor, called the **continental slope**. This in turn lessens in slope as the deep ocean floor is approached; this region is called the **continental rise**. In Figure 1.3 it appears as if these features slope quite steeply, but in fact the actual gradients are very gentle. The continental shelf, slope and rise have average slopes of just 0.1°, 4° and 0.5°, respectively. To put these figures in context, a slope of 4° amounts to a change in height of 7 m over a horizontal distance of 100 m, whereas a slope of 0.1° amounts to a change of just 17 cm over the same 100 m distance. The reason the slopes look so much steeper in Figure 1.3 is that the vertical scale on this cross-section is much greater than the horizontal scale. On the horizontal scale, a distance of 1 cm represents 500 km.

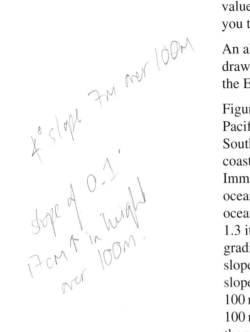

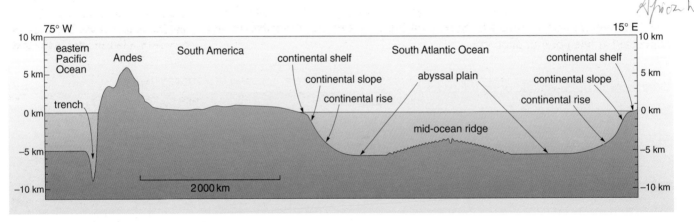

Figure 1.3 Cross-section of the Earth's surface between 20° S, 75° W and 8° S, 15° E.

○ What distance is represented by 1 cm on the vertical scale?

● Measuring the vertical scale with a ruler shows that 1 cm represents 5 km.

The ratio of these two scales is 500 km to 5 km, or 100:1. This means that the vertical scale has been stretched out, or exaggerated, by a factor of 100 relative to the horizontal scale, making gentle slopes appear precipitous. The reason for drawing the cross-section with such pronounced vertical exaggeration is that it allows the topography, or shape of the surface, to be visible on a small diagram.

Beyond the continental rise, and several hundred kilometres from the coastline, lies a flat expanse some 4–6 km below sea-level, as shown by the deeper blue tones on the poster. These areas are called **abyssal plains**: 'abyssal' because they are deep (as in 'abyss'), and 'plain' because they are so flat and extensive. But the abyssal plain does not extend uninterrupted across the Atlantic to the continental rise of South America. The ocean floor shallows considerably to form a broad, elevated region in the mid-Atlantic. This is the same feature you encountered in the North Atlantic when answering Question 1.1. On the poster, you'll see that this feature snakes its way along the mid-Atlantic from south to north, meeting Iceland on the way. This is the Mid-Atlantic Ridge.

Question 1.2

(a) Use Figure 1.3 to estimate the water depth at the crest of the Mid-Atlantic Ridge and at the adjacent abyssal plain. *7km   8km*

(b) What is the height of the ridge above the adjacent abyssal plain? *2km*

It is not just the Atlantic Ocean that contains a large, symmetric ridge. As the poster map shows, a system of **mid-ocean ridges** extends around the Earth. The locations of the mid-ocean ridges are shown in Figure 1.4 along with their names.

Question 1.3

mid atlantic stops on Fig 1.4 - poster sharp up↑

On the poster map, follow the Mid-Atlantic Ridge southwards until it intersects two other ridges. Follow the mid-ocean ridge system eastwards on the poster, noting the names of the most prominent ridges (these are named on Figure 1.4). Are there any mid-ocean ridges to be seen on Figure 1.4 or the poster that are not connected at one point or another?

Figure 1.4 Locations of the major mid-ocean ridges (light blue), ocean trenches (dark blue) and island arcs (red). Trenches and arcs are explained later in the text.

beyond a ridge recommences after Greenland

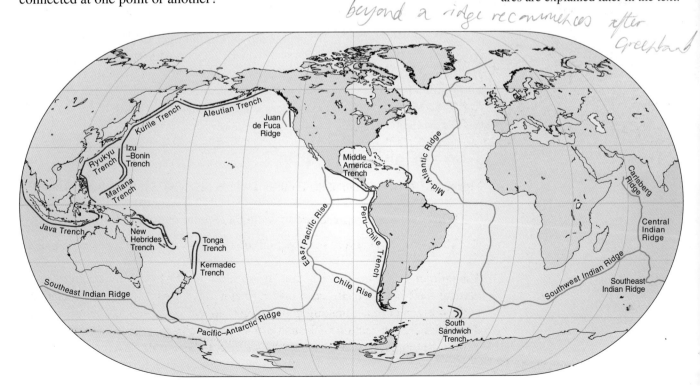

○ Referring to Figures 1.3 and 1.4, in what ways is the ocean floor along the Pacific coast of South America different from that along the Atlantic coast?

● Off the Pacific coast of South America, the continental shelf, slope and rise appear to be absent or at least very much narrower than on the Atlantic coast. Also, the abyssal plain, at about 5 km depth, is separated from the land by a trench some 9 km deep. There is no trench along the east coast of South America.

The name of the deep trench is the Peru–Chile Trench. It is visible on the poster as a narrow dark blue band, about 1 mm wide, running along the eastern margin of the Pacific Ocean adjacent to South America. The western side of the trench is dark, being 'in shadow', whereas the eastern side is 'illuminated' and bright.

The **ocean trenches** are extremely long troughs in the ocean floor, extending from the depth of the abyssal plains to the greatest depths of the oceans. The major trenches are named in Figure 1.4. The Mariana Trench, in the western Pacific Ocean, contains the deepest known point in the oceans (the Challenger Deep) where the ocean floor is 11 034 m below sea-level.

○ How does the depth of the Challenger Deep compare with the height above sea-level of Mount Everest?

● The Challenger Deep is over 2 km deeper than Everest is high!

1.1.3 Island chains and island arcs

Within the ocean basins lie many small islands and submarine mountains. Some are isolated patches of land, but others are arranged together along lines thousands of kilometres long. On the poster map, chains of islands and submarine mountains are particularly noticeable in the Pacific Ocean. Some extend roughly east–west at about 20–30° S. Another prominent chain defines a large 'L'-shape in the northwest Pacific. Still other chains of islands lie alongside some ocean trenches. The chains that lie next to ocean trenches are curved and so are referred to as **island arcs**. Examples are found in the Caribbean, the Aleutian Islands (between Alaska and Siberia) and in the western Pacific, for instance north of New Zealand (visible on the poster).

1.1.4 Heights and depths

So far, we have been considering those parts of the Earth above sea-level separately from those parts below sea-level. But in reality the Earth's solid surface is distributed continuously between the highest point on the continents (8848 m above sea-level) and the lowest point in the oceans (11 034 m below sea-level), a total height difference of almost 20 km.

○ It might seem likely that the height of the Earth's solid surface is equally distributed between these two extremes. From your examination of the poster, do you think that this is correct?

● No. Roughly speaking, most of the Earth's surface is on two main levels — the low-lying land (coloured green on the poster) and the deep ocean floor.

To quantify how much of the Earth's surface area actually lies above, below or between given levels, Figure 1.5 gives a pictorial representation of this information, in the form of a histogram. The length of each bar gives the percentage of the surface area (read from the vertical axis, although the values are also written above each bar) within each 1 km interval. For example, 4.5% of the Earth is at an altitude of between 1 and 2 km above sea-level.

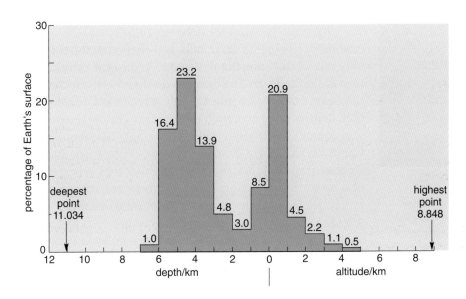

Figure 1.5 A histogram showing the percentage of the Earth's surface area lying within given intervals of height and depth. The percentages of the Earth's surface above 5 km altitude and below 7 km depth are too small to show at this scale. Histograms are discussed further in *The Sciences Good Study Guide*, Chapter 3, Section 2.1.

○ Does the shape of the histogram indicate that the level of the Earth's surface is evenly distributed between the deepest and highest points?

● No, there are two peaks, one centred on 0 to 1 km height and the other centred on 4 to 5 km depth. These peaks indicate that much of the Earth's surface lies within these two height/depth ranges.

○ What is the significance of the trough between the two peaks?

● The trough means that there is only a small portion of the Earth's surface lying at depths between those of the two most common levels.

○ How do these observations compare with the cross-section of the Earth's surface in Figure 1.3?

● They compare well — the most common depths or heights apparent on Figure 1.3 are, on the one hand, the vast expanse of the abyssal plains between 4 and 6 km depth, and, on the other hand, the areas of land and the continental shelves that lie near sea-level (between 1 km deep and 1 km high).

In summary, the histogram illustrates that a substantial proportion of the Earth lies between 3 and 6 km below sea-level, and a second large proportion lies between 1 km depth and 1 km height. Extremely deep regions (ocean trenches) and extremely high regions are rare.

Despite the familiar division of the Earth into areas lying above and below sea-level, the two peaks on the histogram suggest an alternative division placed

Figure 1.6 Basalt columns with polygonal cross-sections: the Giant's Causeway, Co. Antrim, N. Ireland. This feature is so called as it was believed to be the work of the giant Finn McCool, who fell in love with a giant on Staffa, an island in the Hebrides, and he built this wide highway to bring her to Ireland.

between 1 and 2 km depth within the continental rise, not at sea-level. Thus, in this case, the continental shelf, such as that beneath the North Sea and to the west of the British Isles, is really part of the continents rather than the ocean floor. During the last glaciation, when sea-level was some 130 m lower than today, large areas of the continental shelf were actually dry land.

The difference between the deep ocean floor and the continents (including the continental shelf and slope) is not only one of elevation but is also due to the type of material they are made from. The deep ocean floor is covered in sediment, but beneath it lies basalt, which has a relatively high density compared with most rocks. The continents also contain some basalt rock, for example the Giant's Causeway in Antrim, Northern Ireland (Figure 1.6) and the Deccan Traps in India, but a host of other rock types are also found on the continents. These rocks are, on average, less dense than basalt. To an environmental or Earth scientist, the difference between the ocean basins and the continents is not only that one is submerged by seawater, but also that they are made of different types of rock having different densities. In other words, the histogram (Figure 1.5) reveals that the Earth has two geological domains, the continents and the ocean floor, and the boundary between these lies beneath the continental rise, not at sea-level. It so happens that seawater covers the boundary between oceanic and continental rocks; the explanation for this is given in Section 1.3. At the present time about 25% of the continental area is actually covered by the sea.

1.2 Inside the Earth

The Earth's atmosphere and hydrosphere are constantly on the move, fuelled mainly by energy from the Sun. However, the geosphere is also a very active place. Not only are there obvious signs of this activity such as earthquakes and volcanoes, but the surface of the Earth also moves under our feet without most of us ever noticing. This is because the Earth's surface is composed of a dozen or so separate interlocking blocks that are constantly moving around the globe — albeit very slowly. This movement is fuelled by energy stored in the Earth's hot interior. Part of this energy is the heat that remains from the time the Earth formed, called **primordial heat**, but most of the heat is continually produced by a process called radioactive decay. Some of the elements in the Earth, mainly potassium, thorium and uranium, are naturally radioactive, having atoms that spontaneously transform to other isotopes of themselves, or to another element, producing heat in the process.

Question 1.4

Apart from energy from the Sun and the Earth's interior, what other form of energy affects the surface of the Earth?

1.2.1 Compositional layering

Viewed on a global scale, the Earth is composed of concentric layers of differing nature, expressed in two contrasting ways. One is by *composition*, the other is by *mechanical properties*.

The most fundamental compositional distinction within the Earth is between the core, which occupies the centre and is iron-rich, and the overlying rocky material (studied in Block 2). The core consists of inner and outer parts. The inner core is solid and has a density consistent with pure iron, though it may have roughly 20% nickel mixed in. The outer core is liquid and appears to consist of molten iron diluted with around 5–15% of less-dense elements, most likely oxygen and/or sulfur.

Above the core lies the mantle, which is virtually all solid and makes up most of the remainder of the Earth. The distinction between core and mantle is very clear cut, because the mantle consists of silicate minerals and has a bulk chemical composition equivalent to that of a rock type known as peridotite (you examined a sample of this in Block 2, Part 2, number 23 in the *Rock Kit* of the *Digital Kit* DVD).

The outermost solid part of the Earth is the crust. The distinction between crust and mantle is less fundamental than between mantle and core. Crust and mantle are both predominantly silicate in composition, and differ in that the crust has a higher percentage of silica than the mantle, and so is made of less-dense rock. The picture is complicated because the Earth has two distinct types of crust, of differing compositions — continental crust and oceanic crust.

The continental crust is varied and in its upper part shows little tendency towards well-defined internal layering (except in sedimentary rock), whereas oceanic crust has a simpler structure. Part of the reason for this contrast is that most of the continental crust is very old, going back several billion years, and has a complex history, whereas the oldest oceanic crust is only about 180 million years old. This does not mean there was no oceanic crust before that time; rather it is because almost all the oceanic crust older than that has been destroyed by the processes you will meet in Section 1.4. On the other hand, continental crust is virtually indestructible; it can be broken apart, rearranged, deformed and recycled but it cannot be destroyed wholesale as can oceanic crust (Figure 1.7).

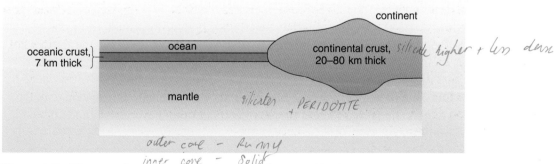

Figure 1.7   The oceanic and continental crust and mantle. The boundary between the two lies below sea-level (around the position of the continental rise), not at the coastline.

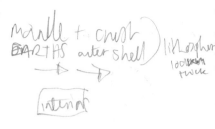

1.2.2 Mechanical layering

The Earth's outer shell moves over its interior. In this context, the outer shell is defined by mechanical properties and consists of the crust and the top few tens of kilometres of the mantle. This combination forms a discrete 'mechanical' unit called the **lithosphere**. *Lithos* means 'rock' in Greek, and the term lithosphere was invented to describe the shell that behaves like rock in the familiar sense of being rigid. The lithosphere is about 100 km thick; it is thinnest under the oceans and thicker below the continents. External forces can cause parts of it to be deformed to produce structures such as mountain belts and mid-ocean ridges.

Below the lithosphere, the rest of the mantle is also made of rock. It, too, is solid rather than molten (in contrast to the outer core), but there is a crucial difference between it and the lithospheric part of the mantle. The prevailing pressure and temperature allow it to behave like a fluid when observed on timescales of centuries or more. The force acting to cause large-scale flow in the mantle below the lithosphere is chiefly the buoyancy force that drives convection, caused by heat generation in the lower mantle. This does not mean that this sub-lithospheric mantle is a liquid. Its rate of flow is very slow, only a few centimetres per year.

The part of the mantle below the lithosphere is known as the **asthenosphere**, *astheno* coming from the Greek for 'weak'. The weakness of the asthenosphere allows lithospheric plates to slide around in the motion described as **plate tectonics**.

1.3 Plates

1.3.1 What is a plate?

The lithosphere is not an intact shell around the Earth; rather it is divided into several large pieces called **plates** (Figure 1.8). Each plate is slowly moving relative to its neighbours at speeds of a few centimetres per year. Plates have earthquakes, faults and deformation at their edges, but relatively little deformation within them.

○ Do plate boundaries coincide with the boundaries between continental and oceanic crust? (Remember that this boundary is around the position of the continental rise, not at the land–sea boundary.)

● In general no, except for the western edge of North, Central and South America.

○ Do all plates have both oceanic and continental lithosphere?

● No, but most plates do. (Some plates have just oceanic lithosphere, e.g. the Cocos and Nazca Plates. There are no plates that have just continental lithosphere.)

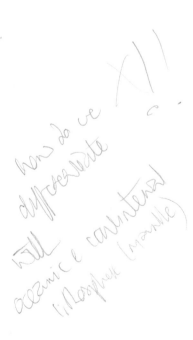

The lithospheric plates move around the Earth over the weaker asthenosphere and this is where the 'tectonics' (the movement and deformation of rock) comes into plate tectonics. The plates move in different directions. The effect of **continental drift** is produced when a plate containing a continent moves relative to a plate containing another continent. For example, the North American continent is part of the North American Plate, whereas Europe is part of the Eurasian Plate. As the

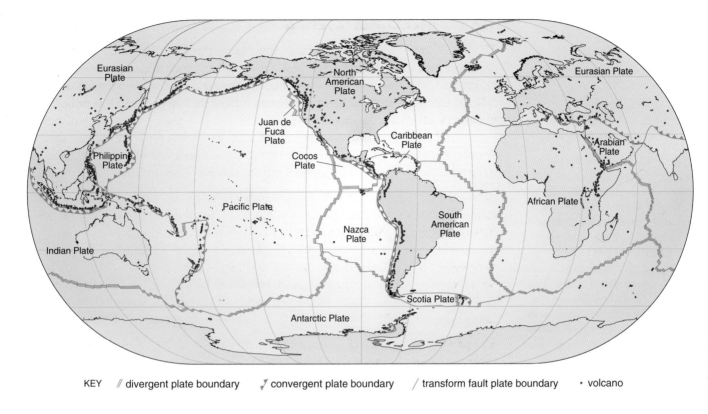

KEY   // divergent plate boundary   ⌄ convergent plate boundary   / transform fault plate boundary   • volcano

Figure 1.8   The Earth's tectonic plates. The terms convergent, divergent and transform fault **plate boundary** identified in the key are defined in Section 1.3.2. The barbs along the convergent plate boundaries are on the plate that is going *over* its neighbour (but note that they point in the direction in which the *underlying* plate is moving).

plates move relative to each other, so do the continents that are part of these plates. The effect of continental drift is therefore explained by plate tectonics.

Because the plates move in different directions they jostle each other at their edges. There the rocks of one plate are moving relative to the rocks of another plate, causing faulting and earthquakes. All the major structural features of the Earth's surface, whether on land or beneath the ocean, are formed as a consequence of plate tectonics.

1.3.2 Plate boundaries

○   Do plate boundaries (shown on Figure 1.8) coincide with any of the major topographic features of the Earth's surface (shown on the poster map and Figure 1.4)?

●   Yes. All mid-ocean ridges are plate boundaries. For example the plate boundary in the Atlantic Ocean between the North American and Eurasian plates is a mid-ocean ridge (the Mid-Atlantic Ridge). All ocean trenches are also plate boundaries; an example is the Peru–Chile Trench off the west coast of South America, which is the boundary between the Nazca and South American plates. Some mountain belts are plate boundaries, for example the Himalayas.

The most prominent topographic features on the Earth are associated with plate boundaries. However, the essence of plate tectonics concerns the relative movement of the plates, and it turns out that plate boundaries can be classified into three types, depending on the direction of relative motion between the plates on each side of the boundary.

At **divergent plate boundaries**, plates are moving away from each other (Figure 1.9a and 1.9d). New lithosphere is added to the plates at the boundary (Section 1.4.1). This is what happens at mid-ocean ridges, so mid-ocean ridges are divergent plate boundaries.

Figure 1.9 The three types of plate boundary, between plates A and B. The motion of each plate is shown by the arrows. (a), (b) and (c) are plan (map) views, and (d), (e) and (f) are block diagrams that give a three-dimensional view of the motion. (a) and (d) show a divergent plate boundary, indicated by the conventional double line symbol. (b) and (e) show a convergent plate boundary, with plates A and B moving towards each other. In this type of convergent boundary, plate B is descending beneath plate A, indicated by the barbs on plate A, the overriding plate. (c) and (f) show a transform fault plate boundary. The single line is the conventional symbol for a transform fault.

The creation of new lithosphere at divergent plate boundaries must be balanced by the destruction of lithosphere elsewhere, otherwise the lithosphere would increase in area and the Earth would expand! Since the Earth is not expanding, lithosphere must be destroyed at the same rate as it is being created. This occurs at another type of plate boundary, a convergent plate boundary.

Along **convergent plate boundaries**, plates are moving towards each other. Figure 1.9b and 1.9e illustrates one form of convergent boundary, where plate B descends below plate A. Where one plate descends beneath another, an ocean trench is formed. A convergent plate boundary of this type may have an ocean trench and a volcanic island arc, like the Japanese islands chain, or an ocean trench and a line of volcanoes along the edge of a continent, like the Andes on the western side of South America. Alternatively, the plates will crumple up and thicken into a mountain belt where they converge, like the Himalayas.

At **transform fault plate boundaries**, plates move past each other in opposite directions (Figure 1.9c and 1.9f). Figure 1.8 shows where the different types of plate boundary are found.

Question 1.5

Roughly how long will it take for the distance between London and New York to increase by 1 km at the current divergence rate for the Eurasian and North American plates of 2.5 cm yr^{-1}?

1.4 Plate movement

1.4.1 Plates moving apart

When two plates move apart at a divergent plate boundary new oceanic lithosphere is created between them in a process named **sea-floor spreading**, as shown in Figure 1.10. This stops a gap opening up. In sea-floor spreading, the divergent plate motion draws the asthenosphere upwards below the plate boundary. As it rises the asthenosphere begins to melt, forming basaltic magma that creates new oceanic crust. The asthenospheric mantle cools as it approaches the surface and adheres at roughly equal rates to the plates on either side of the boundary, becoming part of their lithosphere. This newly formed lithosphere is still relatively warm, making it slightly less dense and thus more buoyant than the older and colder lithosphere that has been displaced further from the boundary. Divergent plate boundaries are therefore marked by elevated ridges on the ocean floor. Typically, the crest of such a ridge is 2–3 km below sea-level, but as it moves away to either side the ocean floor cools and subsides to an average depth of 4–5 km. One of the best-known such ridges is the Mid-Atlantic Ridge that snakes its way from north to south through the Atlantic Ocean and permits the present day east–west divergence of North and South America from Europe and Africa, at a rate of a few centimetres per year.

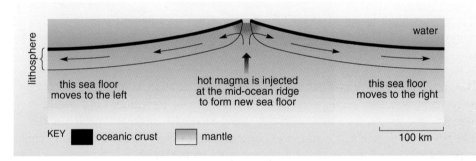

Figure 1.10 The formation of new oceanic lithosphere at divergent plate boundaries by sea-floor spreading.

Divergent motion creates oceanic lithosphere, so divergent plate boundaries are found today only within oceans (Figure 1.8). However, it sometimes happens that divergent motion is initiated within a continent. What happens in such a situation is shown in Figure 1.11. The whole region in Figure 1.11a belongs to a single plate, but by the stage shown in Figure 1.11c the two halves are separated by a divergent plate boundary like that in Figure 1.10, and so belong to two separate plates. What was initially a single continent has rifted into two parts, each joined to new oceanic lithosphere at newly formed continental margins. The time interval between stages (a) and (c) is in the order of 10 Ma.

Figure 1.11 The splitting of a continent by a new divergent plate boundary. In (a) and (b), upwelling within the asthenosphere causes heating and thinning of the continental lithosphere. By stage (c), the continent has rifted apart and a new ocean is beginning to open between them.

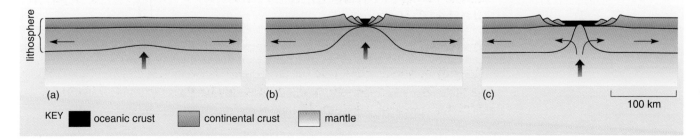

Question 1.6

Where is there a new ocean forming today by the process illustrated in Figure 1.11c? Examine Figure 1.8, the poster and an atlas to answer this.

Mid-ocean ridges may also be the sites for groups of very unusual plants and animals, which only exist because of energy inside the Earth (Box 1.1).

Box 1.1   Hydrothermal vents—deep sea oases where the energy for life comes from inside the Earth

Up to fairly recently, it was thought that the basis of life in the ocean, the primary production, could only take place in the surface waters, where there was sufficient light energy to fuel photosynthesis. However in the late 1970s hydrothermal vents were discovered in the deep ocean. Seawater that circulates through the new, hot ocean crust at mid-ocean ridges heats up, and this hot seawater dissolves and exchanges ions with the basalt rock. In some places along ridges, this mineral-rich hot water vents back into the sea at temperatures of up to about 400 °C. Mixing with cold seawater causes the precipitation of black particles of metal sulfide and oxide (a 'black smoker') or at lower temperatures, white particles of sulfates (a 'white smoker'). These sources of mineral-rich hot seawater support unusual isolated and diverse animal communities (Figure 1.12) in which the primary production that underpins the local food web depends not on photosynthesis, but on chemosynthetic bacteria. The energy for chemosynthesis is derived from the oxidation of sulfide from the hydrothermal vents:

$$CO_2 + H_2S + O_2 + H_2O = [CH_2O] + 2H^+ + SO_4^{2-}$$

from vent fluid   from seawater   carbohydrate

The chemosynthetic bacteria are a source of food for animals that can filter-feed or graze; additionally some vent animals have formed a symbiotic relationship with the bacteria—that is, they provide a home for them in or on their bodies, arranging transport of H_2S to them while

harvesting the bacteria in a sustainable way. For example, the giant tubeworm, *Riftia*, has no mouth, stomach or gut system—it relies entirely on bacteria living within it to provide it with its nutrition. It is estimated that these bacteria comprise about 16% of the tube worm's mass!

Figure 1.12   Tubeworms are a major part of the ecosystems around hydrothermal vents in the Pacific Ocean. The worms are red and can be seen protruding from their tubes, which may reach several metres in length. They have no stomachs, but absorb nourishment from the water with the aid of symbiotic bacteria that live within their bodies. The small crabs in the photo are blind and have no eyes in their eye sockets, which have become adapted into scrapers for scratching off microbes coating the worm tubes, on which they feed.

1.4.2   Plates converging

Convergent plate boundaries involve the most complex of plate boundary processes, and produce the most varied surface features. Part of the variety is caused by the different types of lithosphere that can occur here.

○   The edge of a plate may be made of continental or oceanic lithosphere, so what combinations of lithosphere types might be present at convergent boundaries?

H₂S
hydrogen sulfide

● There are potentially three types of convergent plate boundary: where both edges are oceanic lithosphere, where both edges are continental lithosphere, and where one edge is oceanic and the other continental lithosphere.

Having identified these three types of convergent plate boundary, we shall now have a look at the processes going on there, and ask whether these processes depend on the type of convergent boundary. First we will consider the boundary where one plate has continental lithosphere at the edge and the other plate has oceanic lithosphere. When these two plates are moving towards each other, one of them dives down below the other. But which one?

○ Bearing in mind the relative densities of the two types of crust, which plate would be easiest to force downwards?

● Oceanic crust is denser than continental, so the edge of the plate carrying oceanic crust would tend to go below the continental plate edge.

This situation is illustrated in Figure 1.13. The act of one plate diving below another is termed **subduction** and the relevant part of this plate boundary is described as a **subduction zone**. Subduction destroys the subducting part of the plate.

○ Suggest two reasons why the subducting part of the plate should be destroyed.

● One is that as it gets pushed deeper it will encounter progressively higher temperatures, and begin to melt. Another is that as it encounters higher pressures, the minerals within it are metamorphosed into denser forms. Both processes tend to destroy the integrity of the plate.

Subduction zones are characterized by volcanoes on the overriding plate, a consequence of magma escaping upwards both from the subducting plate and from the base of the overriding plate. The Andes volcanoes of South America are a classic example (Figure 1.14).

When the colliding edges of both plates carry oceanic crust, it is not so obvious which one will be destroyed. Generally speaking, the plate with the oldest, and therefore coldest and densest, oceanic crust is the one to be subducted. When a subduction zone occurs within an ocean, volcanoes appear near the leading edge of the overriding plate, for the same reasons as in an ocean–continent collision. This forms a line of volcanic islands in the ocean, usually in a curved, or arcuate shape, called an island arc.

○ Where do island arcs occur on the Earth?

● From the poster and Figure 1.8 you can see that they are most common in the north and west of the Pacific Ocean, such as the Aleutian Islands and the Philippine Islands. They are also in the Caribbean and South Atlantic, and the northeast Indian Ocean.

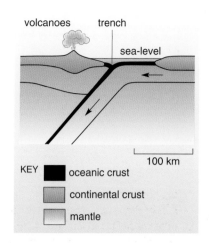

Figure 1.13 A subduction zone convergent plate boundary.

Figure 1.14 Volcano San Pedro, one of the volcanoes along the Andes mountain belt in northern Chile, at a subduction zone.

If volcanism at island arcs (and associated intrusion of igneous rocks at depth) is prolonged, the belt of affected crust can be so thoroughly altered that it becomes more continental than oceanic in character, and in fact this has happened in the case of Japan.

Subduction-related volcanoes occur only on the overriding plate, and tend to be found about 100 km above the subduction zone. Where the two plates meet, the downward bend of the subducting plate means that the ocean floor is particularly deep. The surface expression of a subduction zone is therefore an ocean trench (Section 1.1.2) reaching typically about 8 km below sea-level.

When two plates are converging, the main driving force is believed to be the weight of the relatively dense oceanic lithosphere pulling it below the less-dense continental lithosphere (or the island arc) of the overriding plate. Once this situation is established, there appears to be nothing that can stop it continuing until something really drastic happens. In Figure 1.13, the subducting plate is shown as part oceanic and part continental, with the oceanic part at its leading edge being subducted. What will happen if we wind the clock forward to when all the oceanic lithosphere has been subducted and two continents are colliding?

The weight of the subducting oceanic part of the plate will continue to drive the convergent motion, but now it has to pull down continental crust (Figure 1.15). This is less dense and thus more buoyant than oceanic crust, and cannot be pulled down far. In such a continent–continent collision, the crust is thickened due to a crumpling of the overriding continent and subduction of part of the continental crust of the lower plate. Eventually the oceanic part of the subducting slab may break free, as indicated in Figure 1.15b. The result at the surface is marked by a mountain belt caused by crustal thickening, and often a few slivers of oceanic crust and upper mantle that have avoided subduction. This is just the series of events that have led to the formation of the Himalayan Mountains. The crumpled and thickened crust provides the deep burial and heating required to recrystallize the rocks, so metamorphism occurs in the deep roots of mountain belts formed by continental collision.

○ Look at the map of plate boundaries (Figure 1.8) and the poster map to see if you can identify one other convergent plate boundary where colliding continents have produced a mountain belt along the plate boundary.

● Collision of the Arabian Plate with the Eurasian Plate is associated with the mountain belt running NW–SE from Turkey to the Gulf of Oman.

Figure 1.15 (a) The beginning of continent–continent collision at a convergent plate boundary. (b) Continent–continent collision has forced subduction to cease and a mountain belt is formed. Continuing convergence of the plates will lead to further crumpling and growth of the mountains.

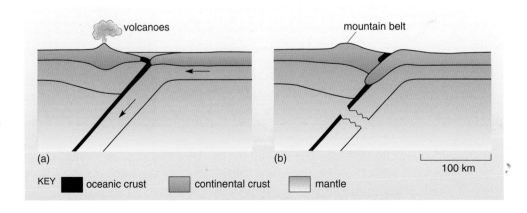

KEY █ oceanic crust ▨ continental crust ░ mantle

1.4.3 Oceans opening and closing

The processes discussed in Sections 1.4.1 and 1.4.2 are combined in Figure 1.16 to illustrate the life cycle of an ocean. In Figure 1.16a, a young ocean is opening. In stage (b), a subduction zone has formed near one side of the ocean. Whether or not the ocean continues to widen depends on the relative rates of subduction and sea-floor spreading. In this example, the two rates are more or less matched so that the ocean stays roughly the same width between stages (b) and (c). However, by the time stage (c) is reached, the divergent plate boundary is close to the subduction zone and will soon be lost. This has happened by stage (d); the ocean basin now lacks a divergent plate boundary, and will eventually be destroyed in a continent–continent collision. The whole cycle is reckoned to take on average about 400–500 million years.

The present northern Atlantic Ocean is at the equivalent of stage (a), having a mid-ocean ridge but no subduction zone. The central Atlantic Ocean may be likened to stage (b), with subduction occurring beneath the Caribbean. The Pacific Ocean is most similar to stage (c). Its divergent plate boundary is displaced to the east side of the ocean, as you can see in Figure 1.8, but the situation is complicated because the Pacific Plate is being subducted on the opposite (western) side of the ocean too.

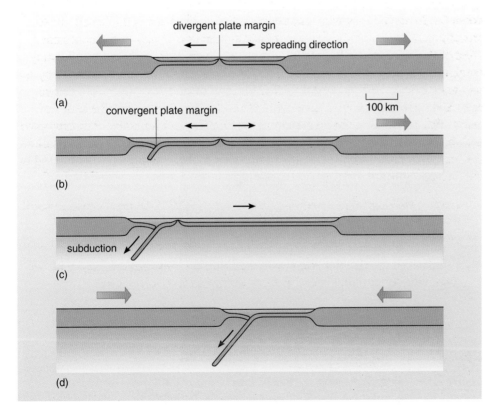

Figure 1.16 Cross-sections of the opening and closing of an ocean. The crust and mantle are not distinguished within the lithosphere.

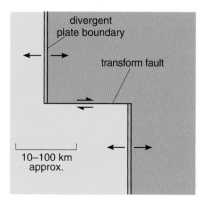

Figure 1.17 Map view of how a transform fault (single line) offsets a divergent plate boundary (mid-ocean ridge, double line) in the oceans. This pattern can be seen on the poster map, most easily in the South Pacific Ocean.

1.4.4 Plates moving sideways

The third type of plate boundary is where adjacent plates slide past each other. In such a situation there is neither creation nor destruction of lithosphere. These boundaries are most common in the oceans, where divergent plate boundaries may be offset by tens or hundreds of kilometres in the form of transform faults (Figure 1.17). They can be seen most easily on the poster in the South Pacific Ocean.

These boundaries can occur within continental crust, too. The San Andreas Fault of California is the most famous example (Figure 1.18), and it is also worth looking back at Figure 1.8 at this stage. This depicts the San Andreas Fault rather schematically. It links the divergent plate boundary between the Pacific Plate and the Cocos Plate to the divergent plate boundary further north between the Pacific Plate and the Juan de Fuca Plate.

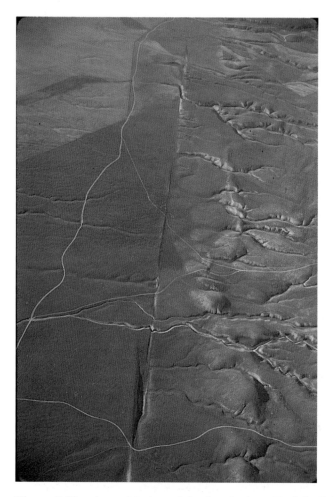

Figure 1.18 An aerial view of the San Andreas Fault in California (the straight feature), looking northwest. The Pacific Plate is to the left of the fault, and the North American Plate to the right of it. The Pacific Plate is moving northwest relative to the North American Plate, producing the linear feature. If you look closely, you can see where the fault has displaced streams and roads. Transform faults produce extensive horizontal linear features on land, but little or no vertical movement.

1.4.5 Why do plates move?

There are a number of factors that cause plates to move and other factors that retard motion. Different speeds arise because the relative importance of these factors varies from plate to plate. To decide what these factors might be, let's start by considering why oceanic lithosphere subducts.

Normally the lithosphere lies on top of the asthenosphere — in fact it floats on the asthenosphere because the crust contains many rock types (e.g. granite) that are less dense than the peridotite in the asthenosphere. However, the density of oceanic lithosphere also depends on how cold it is, and this depends on how old it is. Because oceanic lithosphere is produced by igneous activity at mid-ocean ridges, it is relatively hot when formed. But it cools gradually over many millions of years as sea-floor spreading carries it far from the mid-ocean ridge. As it cools it becomes denser, and the subducting portion of oceanic lithosphere is slightly denser than the asthenosphere. The sinking of the lithosphere into the mantle pulls the rest of the plate with it — an effect called the slab-pull force. Another driving force associated with divergent plate boundaries is provided by the lithosphere sliding off the raised ridge (ridge slide). Counteracting these driving forces is the frictional drag acting on the underside of the plate (Figure 1.19).

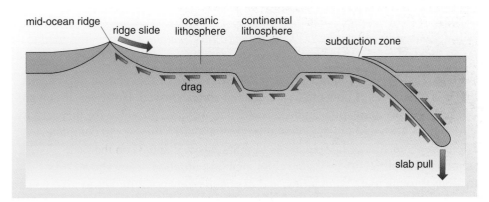

Figure 1.19   A schematic cross-section of a lithospheric plate, labelled with the forces that cause the lithospheric plate to move over the asthenosphere.

1.5 A dynamic Earth

The solid Earth is highly dynamic because of plate tectonics, with plates moving around the surface, creating different surface features. Plates move slowly, at around a few centimetres a year, but on a geological timescale of millions of years this is enough to form oceans and crumple mountain belts.

Plate movement is essentially horizontal on the Earth, whereas mountains have obviously been formed by vertical motion caused by converging plates. How fast does this uplift occur? It is very variable, depending on the two plates involved, but usually slower than the relative horizontal speed of plates. The Himalayas, for example, still forming by the relative movement of the Eurasian and Indian plates towards each other at around $5\,\mathrm{cm\,yr^{-1}}$, are rising at a rate of around $0.5\,\mathrm{cm\,yr^{-1}}$ or $5\,\mathrm{km\,Ma^{-1}}$. As the plates started colliding about $50\,\mathrm{Ma}$ ago, this uplift rate can easily account for the formation of the almost 9 km high Mount Everest.

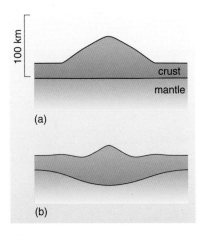

100 km

crust

mantle

(a)

(b)

Figure 1.20 Cross-sections to show how (a) unfeasibly high mountains created by unrealistic thickening at the top of the crust would subside to produce (b) a balanced structure.

There must be another process (or processes) that stops higher mountains forming. The most obvious related process is the one we studied in relation to the formation of sedimentary rocks, weathering. With the subsequent processes of transport of rock debris and deposition elsewhere (combined with weathering into the general term **denudation**) this reduces the height of mountains. Denudation rates are fairly variable, but for the Himalayas are around $0.3 \, \text{cm yr}^{-1}$, close to the uplift rate.

Another process that limits the maximum height of mountains relates to the balance of the lithosphere and the asthenosphere. As the lithosphere is supported by the asthenosphere, when mountains grow by plate collision the weight of the thickened crust forces the asthenosphere to flow from beneath the mountains, so that the lithosphere (and mountains) subside (Figure 1.20).

So the creation of mountain belts, and their development, depends on the relative rates of uplift, denudation and subsidence. All these processes lead to even large-scale landforms having a somewhat ephemeral nature, at least on a geological timescale. Here today, gone tomorrow (or at least in a few million years, or a few hundred million years).

Activity 1.1 Plate tectonics

This activity is based on the DVD sequence *Plate Tectonics*, and is designed to revise and test your understanding of plate tectonic processes.

We hope that by now you have a clear mental picture of the relative movements between plates and of how plates are created and destroyed. However, if you are still puzzled, the animations and exercises that we have provided for this activity should help. It should not take you more than about 15 minutes to complete. There are three animation sequences (animations 1, 2 and 3) on the plate tectonics part of the DVD. Each is less than 20 s duration. They show cross-sections through plate boundaries, and in one the viewpoint moves to give you an oblique view from above. We have not labelled any of them. Your task is to decide (i) which kind of plate boundary or boundaries (divergent, convergent or transform fault) is/are shown in each animation, and (ii) where you would add the following labels: *mid-ocean ridge*, *subduction zone*, *transform fault*, *trench*, *volcano*.

1.6 Summary of Section 1

1   The Earth's solid surface comprises extensive areas of rather flat terrain, principally the oceanic abyssal plains and much of the continental areas. The main linear physical features of the Earth's surface are the mid-ocean ridge system, oceanic trenches, volcanic island arcs and mountain belts.

2   The Earth can be divided into three compositional layers: the crust, mantle and core. The ocean crust is formed of basalt, whereas the continental crust is formed from a wide range of rock types whose mean density is lower than that of basalt. The boundary between the ocean crust and continental crust does not coincide with sea-level, but lies beneath the continental rise.

3   The outer part of the Earth can be divided into two mechanical layers: the rigid lithosphere, consisting of the crust and the uppermost mantle, and the weak asthenosphere underlying it.

4   The lithosphere is divided into fragments called plates. Plate tectonics is a theory that describes how plates interact and move. It incorporates the theory of sea-floor spreading and provides an explanation for continental drift. Plate tectonics is driven by the Earth's internal energy.

5   There are three types of plate boundary, distinguished by the direction of relative motion between two plates. Divergent plate boundaries occur where plates are moving away from each other, creating new oceanic lithosphere, and are found at mid-ocean ridges. Convergent plate boundaries occur where two plates are moving towards each other, and are characterized by an ocean trench and island arc, or an ocean trench and line of volcanoes along the edge of a continent, or a mountain belt. Subducted oceanic lithosphere is destroyed here. Transform fault plate boundaries occur where two plates move past each other in opposite directions.

6   The speeds of relative plate motion are a few centimetres per year.

7   The solid Earth is dynamic, involving horizontal plate motions, vertical uplift, denudation and subsidence.

Learning outcomes for Section 1

Now that you have completed your study of Section 1 you should be able to:

1.1   Recognize the following features on the poster map: mountain belt, continental shelf, continental slope, continental rise, abyssal plain, mid-ocean ridge, ocean trench and island arc. (*Questions 1.1, 1.2 and 1.3*)

1.2   Describe the difference between oceanic crust and continental crust, lithosphere and asthenosphere. (*Activity 1.1*)

1.3   Describe how plate tectonics works to form the large-scale landforms of the Earth in their present locations. (*Questions 1.4, 1.5 and 1.6*)

1.4   Explain how landforms are dynamic features dependent on uplift, denudation and subsidence. (*Activity 1.1*)

2

Introduction to landforms

The landscapes of the Earth are complex systems involving a number of natural processes. Parts of the Earth's surface are raised by tectonic activity and become targets for the destructive forces of water, ice and wind. In fact, the more the surface is raised the faster it is worn down. The resulting debris from nature's onslaught is removed by gravity, wind, flowing ice and water, and transported to the Earth's lower levels. The distinctive features of the Earth's surface that result from these processes comprise the landscape we observe. They include mountains, **valleys**, slopes, plateaux, plains, river beds and dunes, and are termed **landforms** (Figure 2.1).

Figure 2.1   Landforms are complex systems, which reflect a number of processes occurring in the environment. The natural sculptures of Monument Valley, ~~California~~, USA are good examples of this, as the sandstone towers owe their form to the rock they are made of and the forces that act upon them.

lies within Utah e N. Arizona

An appealing image of the formation and destruction of landforms was provided by William M. Davis (1884–1934), who believed that the features in the landscape were taking part in a fixed 'cycle of erosion'. In this model, landforms change in time from 'youth' to 'maturity' and finally 'old age' (Figure 2.2). As Davis saw it, youth begins with uplift and mountain formation. Streams then dissect and wear down this youthful landscape and the area passes through maturity and, eventually, into old age where it becomes a simple undulating lowland with an elevation near sea-level. This 'old age' landscape is given the term **peneplain**, which means 'almost a plain'. At any time, the landscape may be rejuvenated by uplift, which returns an area to the youthful stage of the cycle. Davis believed that landforms are time-dependent and that if the stage of a landform was known, then its past and future development in the cycle of **erosion** could be predicted.

Today, the cycle of erosion with its straightforward uplift of an area followed by a predictable evolution towards a predetermined featureless landscape appears inconsistent with complex processes such as plate tectonics and climate change. It is now generally believed that landforms achieve an equilibrium with the processes that act upon them and if their environment remains the same then they may also remain relatively unchanged, that is they can be time-independent. Hence, as a manifestation of the environment in which they persist, landforms are important indicators and recorders of environmental conditions.

young

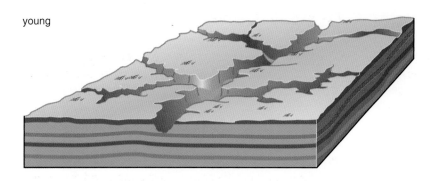

mature

old

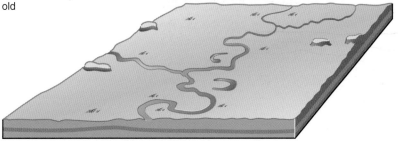

Figure 2.2 William M. Davis's landform 'cycle of erosion'.

2.1 Material transfer and the energy of erosion

A landform system has material introduced and removed through deposition and erosion. Erosion involves the removal of material (soil, sediment, or rock fragments) from a location and deposition takes place when the transported material settles at a new location. Effectively, deposition and erosion provide the inputs and outputs for the landform system.

An example of a landform system in action can be seen in Figure 2.3, which is a digital elevation model looking north over Death Valley, California, USA. Elevation spans from 3368 m above sea-level on the sides to 83 m below sea-level at the valley floor (the lowest point in North America). The effects of erosion and deposition are easily seen in the (bright red) sheets of transported material on the valley sides, which reflect how sediment is being removed from the high mountains and then laid down in alluvial fans on the floor of Death Valley.

Figure 2.3   A digital elevation model looking north over Death Valley, California, USA. The Panamint Mountain Range is on the left, Death Valley is in the centre and the Black Mountains are on the right. The image has been computer enhanced to exaggerate the colour variations that highlight differences in types of surface materials.

For erosion to occur, energy is required. This energy can come from a number of sources, for example the Earth's interior, the Sun's radiation and the gravitational attraction of the Earth, Moon and Sun.

The Earth's internal heat energy drives tectonic activity. Large amounts of this energy are used in mountain building, and this energy is stored in the vast amounts of rock forced above sea-level and temporarily held at higher elevations. The correct term for this stored energy is potential energy. Rock at altitude is out of equilibrium with its surroundings, but its energy can be released as energy of motion or kinetic energy, and equilibrium restored, if the material succumbs to the pull of gravity and falls, rolls, slides, or is otherwise transported to lower elevations.

Radiant energy arrives from the Sun. It causes water to evaporate from the ocean and the land surface, and this may subsequently fall as precipitation at higher elevations where it has a greater amount of potential energy. As ice and water flow from higher to lower levels under the pull of gravity, their potential energy is converted into kinetic energy, the energy of motion, that can erode and transport material on the way. Solar radiation also warms the Earth's surface unequally, initiating convection of the air and creating wind. The kinetic energy of the wind can be used to erode material directly or may be transferred to the sea, to create waves that crash against land in a turbulent zone of energetic activity.

We have considered the direct pull of the Earth's gravity, which encourages uplifted material to make its way as close to the centre of our planet as is physically possible, but this is not the only type of gravitational pull to drive erosion. The gravitational attraction of the Moon, and to some extent the Sun, also has an effect by pulling on the ocean, creating 'tidal bulges'. As the Earth spins on its axis, and the Moon spins around the Earth, these tidal bulges gain kinetic energy as they move around the globe and build up against the continents as tides. In narrow coastal inlets, tides can also generate fast-moving currents. This buffeting of the continental margins and coastlines by tides is actually sapping the Earth of its rotational energy, slowing the Earth down and making days 0.002 s longer each century.

2.2 The erosion process

Erosion can be seen as a sequence of three events: **detachment**, **entrainment**, and **transport**. The face of the Earth is constantly changing as these three events perpetually transfer material from one place to another. However, this transfer does not occur all in one go. In fact, a single particle may undergo detachment, entrainment, and transport many times. Ultimately, particles will finally come to rest following their **deposition** and incorporation into sediments, which are then transformed, by burial and compaction, into solid rock.

2.2.1 Detachment

Erosion begins with detachment, where a piece of rock is released from the rock around it to become an unattached rock fragment. Detachment can be achieved through physical, chemical or biological processes.

Physical weathering leads to detachment by purely mechanical means, which can occur in many different ways. **Hydraulic action** is related to the force of water surging into cracks or, if the rock is not completely submerged, the compression of air in cracks and crevices that can expand explosively when the water retreats. **Attrition** occurs when rock fragments collide against each other and get shattered into progressively smaller pieces. Rock fragments impacting against the bedrock bring about **abrasion**, breaking rock down thereby releasing more fragments. The collapse of bubbles in rapidly moving and turbulent water, a process called **cavitation**, generates a shock wave that can fragment solid rock. As we saw earlier in Block 2, Part 2, frost shattering occurs when water freezes, and the resulting increase in volume forces the rock apart, while **salt weathering** is found where the growth of salt crystals within rock pore spaces performs the same function. **Plucking** occurs when ice freezes onto the surface of chunks of rock and in the cracks and crevices around them and then plucks the blocks out as it moves.

Chemical weathering breaks down minerals that formed at higher temperatures and pressures, and transforms them into new minerals that are more stable in conditions at the Earth's surface. One of the most crucial factors in chemical weathering is the ease with which water can enter a rock. The materials from rocks can then be dissolved by the process of solution.

Different physical and chemical weathering processes occur with different erosive agents (Table 2.1). Once physical or chemical weathering have released fragments they are more susceptible to the next step in the erosion sequence, entrainment.

○ Which detachment process occurs with all erosive agents?

● Abrasion.

○ According to Table 2.1, which erosive agent brings about most detachment processes?

● Water.

Table 2.1 The relationship between detachment processes and the erosive agents.

Process	Water	Ice	Wind
hydraulic action	✔		
abrasion	✔	✔	✔
attrition	✔		✔
cavitation	✔		
solution	✔		
frost shattering		✔	
salt weathering	✔		✔
plucking		✔	

Biological weathering can facilitate detachment by providing cracks and fissures that may be exploited by physical and chemical weathering. Seeds are able to germinate in small cracks and grow into plants whose roots penetrate and separate the rock mass. The destructive effect of tree roots near walkways, garden walls and buildings is a potent reminder of this process. Large and small burrowing animals also aid detachment by bringing rock particles to the land surface, exposing them to chemical and physical action.

2.2.2   Entrainment

Entrainment is the process that lifts particles off the surface and sets them in motion. It is often difficult to identify a point of distinction between detachment and entrainment. Entrainment is resisted by friction between the particle and its neighbours, and by the force of gravity, which may hold it in place. Material is entrained by the drag created by the movement of the transporting medium flowing over the particle. The strength of drag and its effect on resting particles varies with the mass of the transporting medium and its speed. Drag can be thought of here as horizontal (pushing) and vertical (lifting) forces (Figure 2.4). If these forces are sufficient to overcome the horizontal resistance of friction and vertical resistance of gravity, the particle will begin to move.

Figure 2.4   The forces acting on a particle at rest in a fluid.

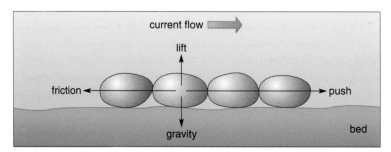

In wind and water, turbulent eddies assist entrainment by penetrating down between, and disturbing, the resting particles. Once a particle is in motion the forces required to transport it are less than those necessary to achieve entrainment, due to the smaller amounts of frictional resistance. The critical speed at which entrainment occurs is related to grain size, and this can be illustrated by a Hjulström diagram (Figure 2.5).

Figure 2.5   The Hjulström diagram illustrates that the fluid flow speed required to entrain a particle is related to the grain size, and that once entrainment has occurred the speed required to sustain movement is less. Note the logarithmic scales.

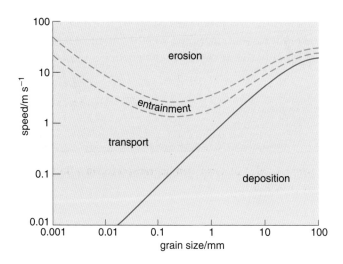

○ Which grain sizes require the highest speeds to be entrained?

● The smallest and the largest.

It is easy to understand why the entrainment of large particles requires higher flow speeds. Larger particles are likely to be heavier and, therefore, will require more energy to be lifted off a surface. Why the very finest particles require high flow speeds to be entrained is, perhaps, less obvious. Fine particles are difficult to entrain because they have very strong cohesive forces that are far greater than the forces of friction and gravity.

2.2.3 Transport

Once material is entrained, it tends to continue moving as long as the speed of wind, water or ice is high enough to transport the particle horizontally. Transport can occur in four different ways: **solution**, **suspension**, **saltation** and **traction** (Figure 2.6). All these modes of transport reflect the conflict between the pull of the Earth's gravity, which seeks to bring a particle to rest, and the drag of the transporting medium, which encourages particle movement.

Some eroded material is dissolved and transported in the water as individual ions. This type of transport is called solution and it occurs only in aqueous environments. The finest solid particles are often transported without returning to the bed, and this mode of transport is termed suspension, and can occur in air, water, and ice. Some particles move forward by a series of short jumps, returning to the bed periodically; this bouncing mode of transport is seen in air and water and is referred to as saltation (from the Latin *saltare* 'to leap'). Additionally, in all transporting agents, particles can roll, slide and shuffle along the bed in a process called traction. In all the cases above, it is the mass, size and shape of the particle, and the type and speed of transporting agent, that determines which of these processes operate.

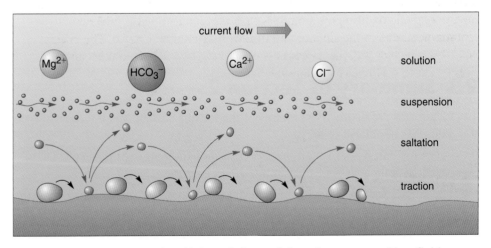

Figure 2.6   The four ways in which eroded material can be transported in a fluid: solution, suspension, saltation and traction.

2.2.4 Deposition

The transport of a particle does not occur as a single continuous process. In fact, it is more likely that entrainment, transport, and deposition will occur repeatedly for any given particle. Transport will continue until there is a reduction in the speed of the medium or an increase in the resistance of the particles. If either of these occurs, the ability of the medium to transport will be reduced and deposition will be the result. Fluids can experience a local drop in speed due to the sheltering effect of obstructions such as rocks, hills or vegetation. More widespread changes in speed may occur because of large-scale reductions in the speed of the fluid, for example, when a river meets an estuary. Wind speed is driven by temperature and pressure differences between adjacent areas. If these differences become less pronounced, wind speed is reduced. In a similar fashion, the speed of flowing water or ice may drop due to a decrease in the amount of precipitation falling in an area.

Two depositional processes specific to water are precipitation and flocculation. **Precipitation** occurs where dissolved substances become solid and settle out, perhaps because of a change in temperature, or are converted to insoluble materials through chemical processes taking place in the water. **Flocculation** is a process where solid particles of colloidal (< 1 μm) dimensions, suspended in a liquid, come together to form loose aggregations or soft flakes. This process is especially common where freshwater and saltwater mix, causing fine clays to clot and sink through the water column, and is in part due to differences in the chemistry of the two water bodies involved.

Now that the underlying processes of landform creation have been dealt with, we will focus on what may be called the agents of change: water, ice and wind. We want to explore how, individually, these agents erode, transport and deposit material and what effect they have on the physical appearance of the land. Where possible we will attempt to highlight how the physical form of the land can be attributed to specific agents of change operating within a particular set of environmental conditions. Using this approach, landforms become diagnostic features that act as a tangible record of the environment.

2.3 Summary of Section 2

1   Landforms are distinctive features of the Earth's surface and are the result of a number of natural processes.

2   Landforms are systems that involve the input and output of material. They persist as long as inputs and outputs are balanced.

3   The energy for the transport of material into and out of the landform system comes from three sources: the Earth's internal heat, solar radiation and gravity.

4   The process of erosion can be divided into four steps: detachment, entrainment, transport and deposition.

Learning outcomes for Section 2

Now that you have completed your study of Section 2 you should be able to:

2.1 Explain how landforms are manifestations of processes occurring in an environment and, therefore, constitute a valuable and interpretable record of prevalent conditions.

2.2 Describe how landforms are systems that involve the input and output of material.

2.3 List the different sources of energy for material transfer.

2.4 Explain how the erosion process can be divided into four steps: detachment, entrainment, transport and deposition.

3 Lithology and landforms

We have seen how the movement of tectonic plates can generate impressive large-scale landforms, particularly at the plate margins. But even at much smaller scales the bare bones of any landscape are provided by the geology that lies underneath. The fracturing and buckling of the Earth's crust occurs on all scales to create faults and folds that range from centimetres to many kilometres in size. When big enough, these structural features are often evident at the Earth's surface.

3.1 Structural landforms

As far as we are concerned the term '**structural landform**' refers to those landforms that are controlled by the geology of the bedrock. Folds occur when beds of compressed rock bend rather than break and in the early stages may form ridges and valleys. **Faults** are fractures in the Earth's crust along which displacement has occurred. If the fault plane is exposed it can form a fault scarp (Figure 3.1a). When a fault block drops down between two adjacent blocks, much as the keystone in an arch will fall if the walls of the arch move apart, a **horst and graben** structure is formed (Figure 3.1b). This process is responsible for the East African Rift Valley, where the valley floor lies 1000 m or more below the surrounding plateaux of Ethiopia and Kenya.

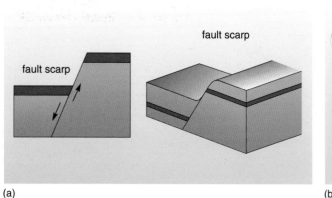
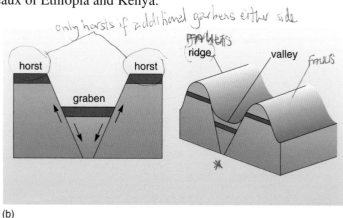

(a)   (b)

Figure 3.1   Some simple landforms that reflect faulting in the underlying structural geology: (a) a fault scarp, (b) a ridge and valley system reflecting a horst and graben structure.

3.2 Igneous landforms

Igneous landforms are those landforms reflecting igneous activity that has introduced molten rock into either surface or subsurface environments. The molten material may solidify within (intrusive) or on the surface of (extrusive) the land to produce a dramatic landform (Figure 3.2).

For example, a volcano forms where igneous material erupts through the crust, and a lava plateau may result from the solidified sheets of lava it produces. In contrast, the effects of intrusive igneous rocks may only become obvious once erosion has removed their less resistant surrounding materials. When lava solidifies in the core of the volcano a volcanic neck is produced, and when

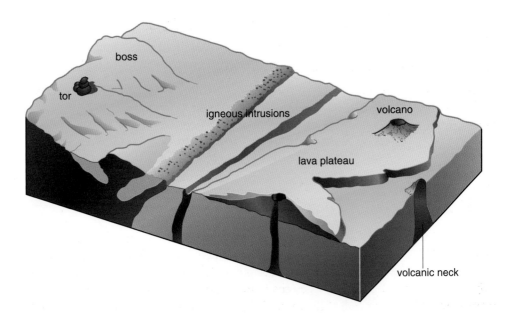

Figure 3.2 Various igneous landforms, some of which are generated from eruptions of molten rock at the surface, while others only become apparent once uncovered by erosion.

igneous material is injected into the surrounding bedrock it can form vertical or horizontal igneous intrusions. If the molten rock 'ponds' in the subsurface to form a circular intrusion it will form a boss, which, once exposed, may be weathered to give a tor, such as those seen in southwest England, UK (Figure 3.3).

Figure 3.3 Granite Tor near Cheesewring, Bodmin Moor, UK.

3.3 Lithology and landscape

Sometimes the main landforms in an area are a direct response to the rock type from which they are made as different rocks weather in different ways. **Karst** landscapes are perhaps the most famous lithologically controlled landscape (Figure 3.4). Karst areas are characterized by barren, rocky ground with rock towers, caves, complex underground drainage systems and the absence of surface streams and lakes. The term karst is derived from a limestone area on the Dalmatian coast adjacent to the Adriatic Sea where all these features were first noted. Conditions that promote a karst landscape are those that encourage the chemical and physical erosion of rocks, i.e. well-fractured dense limestone or evaporites, a moderate to heavy rainfall and good groundwater circulation.

Figure 3.4 Karst landscape in Malaysia where the landforms are mainly produced by dissolution of the carbonate bedrock.

3.4 Summary of Section 3

1 Structural geology of the crust can determine the topography at the Earth's surface. Distinctive features resulting from these effects can be called structural landforms.

2 Igneous landforms are those that have a characteristic shape due to the form taken by the original molten rock as it solidified.

3 The lithology of an area may have a strong influence on the rates and types of erosion; whole landscapes may be characterized by their landforms.

Learning outcomes for Section 3

Now that you have completed your study of Section 3 you should be able to:

3.1 Explain the role of geology in producing landforms.

3.2 Identify that specific lithologies can result in distinctive landforms.

Water: fluvial landforms

When we recall images of the sunlight reflecting on open bodies of water such as lakes and oceans it is easy to imagine how energy from the sun evaporates water from lower levels and how water vapour may be transported to higher altitudes where this water then falls onto the land as rain or snow. Recall from your studies in Block 3, Part 1 that this is an important part of the hydrological cycle. Although it is not only on open bodies of water where evaporation operates, low-lying clouds of water vapour liberated from thick forests by morning sunlight (Figure 4.1) are strong reminders that the transformation of liquid water to gas is also a significant process on land. But wherever the source of the water, when it is deposited high above sea-level it begins a journey back to the level from which it originated, drawn by the pull of gravity.

Figure 4.1 Clouds of water vapour are generated as morning sunlight warms moisture-laden forests in the Vincentian Alps, Italy.

If we know, roughly, the mass of water precipitated and the average altitude at which the precipitation occurred, we can perform a simple calculation to reveal the potential energy that has been gained by the water. (Remember from Block 2, Part 1 that:

$$\text{potential energy} = mgh \qquad (4.1)$$

where m = mass in kg, g = acceleration due to gravity: $9.8\ \mathrm{m\,s^{-2}}$ and h is height in metres.)

○ The average height of the Earth's surface is about 750 m above sea-level and it has been estimated that the amount of water that falls on the land each year is around 4 100 000 000 kg. Calculate the potential energy of the Earth's precipitation on land each year.

● Potential energy of the precipitation on land = mgh
  = 4 100 000 000 kg × 9.8 m s^{-2} × 750 m
  = 3.0135×10^{13} kg m^2 s^{-2}
  or (because 1 N = 1 kg m s^{-2} and 1 Nm = 1 J) 3.0135×10^{13} J.

Ultimately, this is energy that has been given to the water via the Sun's radiation. This potential energy is converted into the kinetic energy of flow of all the streams draining the land. But not all this energy produces erosion: it has been estimated that over 90% of the potential energy of a river flowing to the sea is dissipated as internal turbulence within the water itself. This leaves less than 10% of the potential energy (3.0135×10^{12} J) available to erode and transport rock particles. Of course, the whole process is continuous. The hydrological cycle will turn as long as the Sun shines, providing radiant energy to evaporate water, and perpetual erosion, transportation and deposition will be the by-product. It is because of this process that streams are the prime transporters of rock from the land to the ocean, and it is an almost inescapable fact that today's Alpine-scale mountain tops will be tomorrow's gentle foothills.

4.1 Fluvial processes

4.1.1 Stream flow

Processes related to the movement of water in streams and rivers are given the term fluvial, from the Latin *fluvius* for river. From now on, for simplicity, we will use the term 'stream' to describe either a stream or a river. The ability of fast-flowing streams to erode the land is obvious, but erosion by water can begin long before a distinct stream has formed. The impact of raindrops on the ground dislodges small particles that gradually travel downslope under the pull of gravity. The movement generated by one raindrop is relatively small, but the sheer amount of raindrops make this a significant process — quite literally an example of 'strength in numbers'. We saw earlier in the course that some rainwater evaporates or sinks into the ground but the remainder becomes runoff. It is the surface-sited runoff that we will consider here. Runoff either moves as interconnected finger-shaped 'rills' or as broad sheets of water. The erosion resulting from runoff is called **sheet erosion** because it progressively strips sheets of unconsolidated material from the land.

○ Can you think why erosion caused by runoff is less common on vegetated land?

● Vegetation cover, especially by plants such as grasses that have dense root networks, binds material together. Plant leaves also intercept the falling rain, cushioning the land beneath and holding onto the water long enough so that it can seep into the ground.

Once water moves over the surface within the walls of well-defined channels it becomes **stream flow**, and the eroded material transported by the stream is known as the **stream load**.

4.1.2 Stream load

Some of the eroded material that makes up the stream load is dissolved in the water to produce the stream's **dissolved load.** The bulk of the dissolved load usually consists of ions such as hydrogen carbonate (HCO_3^-), calcium (Ca^{2+}), sulfate (SO_4^{2-}), chloride (Cl^-), magnesium (Mg^{2+}), sodium (Na^+) and potassium (K^+).

○ Which factors will influence the amount and type of material in a stream's dissolved load?

● The rock types in the area and the amount of groundwater that has found its way into the stream. Rocks like limestone dissolve more readily than do basalts, and water that has travelled through the ground has had more time to dissolve its surroundings.

The remaining part of the stream's load is not dissolved, and consists of solid particles transported by the stream. Water flowing through a channel pushes and lifts the grains that make up the channel bed and sides. The grains will only begin to move when the force of the water overcomes both the force of gravity holding the materials down and the friction between individual grains and the stream bed. How material is carried along depends on the way the water itself is flowing. You will recall from Block 3, Part 1 that there are two types of flow: laminar and turbulent. During laminar flow, individual parts of the fluid move in straight lines parallel to each other, whereas turbulent flow involves the parcels of fluid moving in a more chaotic fashion, sometimes upwards and sometimes downwards to create complex eddies, even though the overall flow is in one direction. You will also recall that faster moving water is more turbulent than water that flows slowly.

○ Which type of flow, laminar or turbulent, do you think is more effective at transporting particles?

● Turbulent flow, as it helps to transport stream load by creating vortices and eddies that lift and support particles.

Almost all streams have turbulent flow, and the finest particles are caught up in turbulent eddies to remain in suspension for relatively long periods of time and form the **suspended load**. Suspended load is measured by taking samples of water at various depths and using filters of known sizes to separate out the suspended material; both the volume and average particle size of a suspended load can be calculated in this way.

Some streams have so much suspended load that it determines their colour. For example, the Yellow River (Huang Ho) of China is yellow because of the large amount of suspended material it contains (Figure 4.2). This material is eroded from the widespread deposits of wind-blown dust that form the landscape of the basin. Remarkably, when the Yellow River is in flood, the mass of suspended load may be greater than the mass of water. However, the Yellow River is not the world's greatest carrier of suspended load, this position is occupied by the mighty Ganges and Bramaputra rivers (Box 4.1).

Figure 4.2 The mouth of the Yellow River (centre of image), China, with its suspended load clearly visible.

Box 4.1 The world's stream load

Little drops of water,
Little grains of sand,
Make the mighty ocean
And the beauteous land.

Julia A. Carney, *Little Things*, 1845

Material transported by streams and rivers amounts to between 13.5×10^{12} and $16.2 \times 10^{12} \, \text{kg yr}^{-1}$. Expressed as an average, each square kilometre of drainage basin on land provides 1.5 to $1.8 \times 10^5 \, \text{kg}$ of sediment that ends up in the sea. However, this average value hides significant regional variations. For example, on average the Ganges and Brahmaputra rivers in northern India account for over 12% of the global annual suspended load. The Yellow River in China comes a close second with a share of over 8%. Figure 4.3 shows the Brahmaputra River running from the east (top left) into the Bay of Bengal (top right) while the Ganges drains from the west (bottom) to the same point. The Himalayas are the large snow-capped peaks along the left side of the figure. The high values of suspended load are due to the mountainous terrain and heavy rainfall.

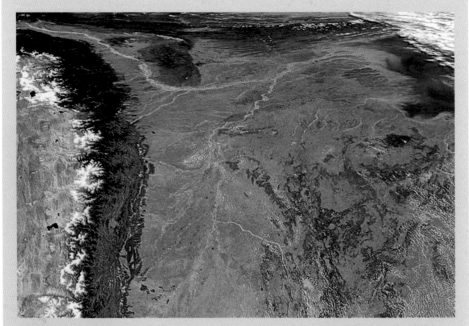

Figure 4.3 The Ganges and Brahmaputra river valleys draining away from the Himalaya mountains.

The particles in a stream that are not moved in solution or suspension are known as the **bedload** (Figure 4.4), and these respond to turbulence by bouncing, rolling and sliding along in the direction of water flow.

Intermediate sized particles in the bedload that are too big to be held in suspension bounce along the stream bed by saltation. Saltation will continue as long as the flow is turbulent enough to pull particles off the bed and permit them to travel some distance downstream.

Figure 4.4 The bedload of a stream in Colorado, USA, being subjected to scrutiny. These large objects are moved, by the higher flow, at times of flood.

○ What happens to the part of the bedload that is too big to be transported by suspension?

● This material will simply roll or slide along the stream bed.

The absolute amount of bedload in a stream is difficult to measure and requires expensive sediment traps which are placed on the stream bed for certain lengths of time before being retrieved and the collected load studied. Measuring the average size of the bedload particles is much easier and involves taking a selection of bedload material, measuring the dimensions of the particles, and calculating a mean value.

4.1.3 Competence and capacity

If you were to wade out into the centre of a stream and examine the bedload beneath your feet, there would be a range of particle sizes. The size of the largest particle reflects the **competence** of the stream. Generally, competence increases with water speed, but not in a simple linear fashion. The largest particle moved by the stream varies to the sixth power of the speed.

○ If the speed of a stream is doubled, what effect will this have on its competence?

● Doubling the speed increases the competence 2^6 (64) times.

This is why floods can move large rocks, boulders, bridges and cars.

Although competence tells us about the size of individual objects that can be moved by a stream, it tells us less about the overall amount of material that is being transported. This amount is reflected by the **capacity** and is measured as the volume of sediment passing a given point in a stream channel at any one time. Capacity depends on (i) discharge (the amount of flow in cubic metres per second), (ii) speed (often determined by gradient and reduced by lakes and seas), and (iii) the cross-sectional area of the stream.

4.2 Stream morphometry

The measurement of the shape of any natural object is termed morphometry. When this approach is applied to streams and rivers it is called fluvial morphometry. Look at a map of a drainage basin, as in Figure 4.5: the network of channels resembles the branches of a tree. But, just as networks of branches can differ from tree to tree, the network of channels are often dissimilar in different drainage basins. The idea that you could use these variations between stream networks to compare and contrast different drainage basins was developed by Robert E. Horton, an American hydraulic engineer and hydrologist. Horton's system was later modified by Arthur N. Strahler to give us the system that is commonly used today (Figure 4.5).

Figure 4.5 The Strahler stream ordering system applied to a small drainage basin.

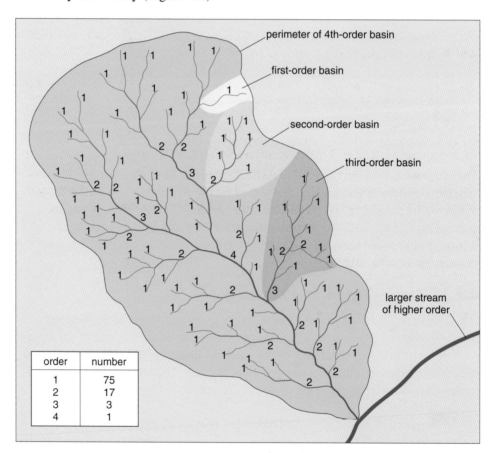

order	number
1	75
2	17
3	3
4	1

4.2.1 Stream order

Horton and Strahler recognized that the arrangement and dimensions of streams in a drainage basin tend to be orderly. This can be illustrated by studying a map of a drainage basin and assigning numbers, or 'orders', to stream sections based on their position in the system. The smallest stream segments, that exhibit no branching, are designated as first-order streams. Two unbranched first-order streams combine to give a second-order stream and when two second-order streams unite they form a third-order stream, and so on. Keep in mind that it takes two streams of the same order to raise the order of the downstream channel. This means that a third-order stream can have numerous first and second-order tributaries, but it will only become a fourth-order stream when it meets another third-order stream. The drainage basin itself can be described according to its highest order stream. So, for example, Figure 4.5 in its entirety represents a fourth-order basin. The use of stream orders to describe drainage basins quickly led Horton to recognize two laws for drainage basin networks.

The **law of stream numbers** states that higher order streams are less abundant than lower order streams, and the decrease in abundance occurs in a regular fashion. Let us begin to examine the law of stream numbers by looking at the relationship between streams of different order. The ratio between the number of stream segments in one order and the next, is called the bifurcation ('dividing into two') ratio:

$$R_b = N_u/N_{u+1} \tag{4.2}$$

Where R_b is the bifurcation ratio, N_u is the number of streams of a given order, and N_{u+1} is the number of streams of the next highest order.

○ If a drainage basin had 81 first-order stream segments and 27 second-order stream segments, what would be the value for R_b?

● R_b would be 3.0.

R_b is generally between 3 and 5, as shown in Table 4.2. The data in Table 4.2 are derived from a carefully studied large-scale map of a single drainage basin in the Big Badlands of South Dakota, USA. All the stream segments were assigned orders and the numbers of segments of each order were counted.

Table 4.2 Stream orders and bifurcation ratios for a drainage basin in the Big Badlands, USA.

Stream order (u)	Number of stream segments (N_u)	Bifurcation ratio (R_b)
1	139	3.0
2	46	4.2
3	11	3.7
4	3	3.0
5	1	

○ What is the average R_b for the Big Badlands drainage basin?

● The average R_b is 3.5, which is within our 3 to 5 range.

Now that we understand that R_b is relatively constant, between 3 and 5 in all drainage basins, we can consider Horton's original definition of the law of stream numbers:

> The numbers of stream segments of successively lower orders in a given basin tend to form a geometric series, beginning with a single segment of the highest order and increasing according to a constant bifurcation ratio.

In other words, as we go up an order, the number of stream segments decreases so as to maintain a constant ratio of around 3 to 5.

Horton's law of stream numbers can be expressed mathematically as:0

$$N_u = R_b^{(k-u)} \tag{4.3}$$

Where N_u is the number of streams of a given order, R_b is the bifurcation ratio, k is the highest order stream, and u is the stream order.

Question 4.1

There are six orders of stream in a drainage basin. There is one sixth-order stream and three fifth-order streams. Assume a constant R_b of 3.0 and estimate the numbers of streams of fourth, third, second and first order.

The **law of stream lengths** suggests that higher order streams are longer than lower order streams and the increase in length occurs in a regular way. To convince yourself of this point refer back to Figure 4.5. The mean length of stream segments increases by a ratio of roughly 3 with each increase in stream order. This proportion of increase is known as the length ratio (symbol R_L) and is relatively constant for a given drainage basin. We can define R_L as follows:

$$R_L = L_u/L_{u-1} \tag{4.4}$$

Where L_u is the mean length of all stream lengths of order u, and L_{u-1} is the mean length of all stream lengths of the next lowest order.

Now we are in a position to look at Horton's definition of the law of stream lengths.

> The cumulative mean lengths of stream segments of successive orders tend to form a geometric series beginning with the mean length of first-order segments and increasing according to a constant length ratio.

The term 'cumulative' simply means that the mean lengths are added progressively (cumulated) as we go from a lower to higher order.

Question 4.2

There are six orders of streams in a drainage basin. The sixth-order stream is 243 km long and the fifth-order stream is 81 km long. Assume a constant R_L of 3.0 and estimate the lengths of streams of fourth, third, second and first order.

Horton's law of stream lengths can be expressed mathematically by the equation:

$$L_u = L_1 R_L^{(u-1)} \tag{4.5}$$

Where L_1 is the mean length of all stream lengths of the first order. All other terms have been previously defined.

Question 4.3

To consolidate your understanding of the law of stream numbers and the law of stream lengths complete Table 4.3 for the Allegheny River drainage basin, Pennsylvania, USA.

Table 4.3   Characteristics of the Allegheny River drainage basin, Pennsylvania, USA.

Stream order (u)	Number of stream segments (N_u)	Bifurcation ratio (R_b)	Mean length (km) of segments (L_u)	Cumulative mean length (ΣL_u)	Length ratio (R_L)
1	5966	*3·90*	0.16		–
2	1529	*4·04*	0.48		
3	378	*5·56*	1.29		
4	68		4.02		
5	13		11.26		
6	3		32.20		
7	1	–	112.6		

In addition to stream ordering, various aspects of drainage network forms were found to be quantifiable. One such relationship was drainage density. Drainage density is a measure of the length of stream channel per unit area of drainage basin. This **law of drainage density** is expressed as:

$$D_d = \Sigma(N_u \times L_u)/A_b \qquad (4.6)$$

Where D_d is drainage density in km km^{-2}, $\Sigma(N_u \times L_u)$ is total stream length in km and A_b is basin area in km^2.

A drainage density value of, say 15, indicates that for every square kilometre of basin there are 15 km of stream channels. The measurement of drainage density provides a hydrologist or geomorphologist with a useful numerical measure of landscape dissection and runoff potential. On a highly permeable or vegetation-rich landscape, with small potential for runoff, drainage densities are sometimes less than 1 km km^{-2}. On impermeable or unvegetated landscapes, highly dissected surfaces are found and densities of over 500 km km^{-2} are often reported (Figure 4.6).

Closer investigations of the processes responsible for drainage density variation have discovered that two factors influence stream density. The first is the amount of water that is received at the land surface and this is obviously controlled by climate. The second is the ease with which water can cut channels in the ground. Channel formation is controlled by topography, soil, vegetation and geology.

Figure 4.6   Badlands of South Dakota showing a very high drainage density.

4.2.2   Stream patterns

The shape of a stream system provides evidence of the geological and topographical factors that have been involved in its formation and development. Stream patterns also reveal something about the age of the stream system, with some only being found on recently exposed land. Different types of stream pattern are shown in Figure 4.7.

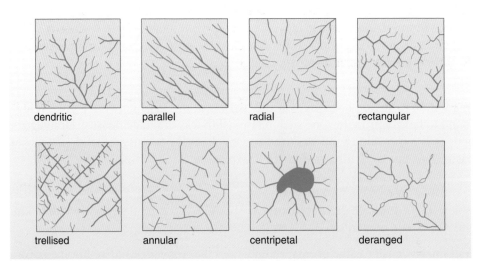

Figure 4.7   Stream patterns.

Dendritic stream systems are characterized by irregular branching. This 'tree like' pattern indicates that the system has grown undisturbed by the underlying rock types. Dendritic stream systems are usually large and highly integrated, reflecting their relatively old age. **Parallel** systems are a young and simple type of drainage pattern that forms on the uniformly sloping surfaces of single rock types. Parallel streams are often seen on freshly exposed, gently sloping roadside cuttings. With time, parallel systems develop into larger and more integrated dendritic systems. **Radial** stream systems have channels that look like the spokes of a wheel; the channels all radiate out from a single topographic high, such as a dome or volcanic cone. Radial systems tend also to become more complex with age. **Rectangular** stream systems have sharp, right-angled bends and are formed on the heavily fractured surfaces of hard rocks. The stream channels exploit the relatively erodable fractures. **Trellis** stream patterns result from alternations of hard and soft bands of bedrock. The positions of the soft beds are followed by long, parallel tributaries, which resemble vines trained on a trellis. This type of drainage is also known as the Appalachian drainage pattern because it is characteristic of the Appalachian Mountains in the USA. Where alternating beds of hard and soft rock are forced into a dome, **annular** streams form almost circular channels around the dome. The streams exploit the erodable beds. If streams converge towards a central depression, such as a volcanic crater, then they form a **centripetal** pattern. When stream systems show a complete lack of adjustment to the underlying structure and rock types they are called **deranged**. This type of stream pattern is characteristic of a very young system. Deranged stream systems are common on recently deglaciated land where runoff collects in basins formed by glacial deposits; the streams follow the local, often random, gradients.

4.3 The stream profile

The **long profile** of a stream is a line that shows the gradient of its water surface from the source to the sea. The long profile of a stream is longer than the long profile of the valley in which the stream flows, as the valley profile does not take account of the bends in the stream. Given enough time all streams produce a concave upwards long profile, which is steep near the source and almost flat near the sea. The Red Deer River in southern Alberta, Canada shows the concave long profile characteristic of a **graded stream** (Figure 4.8). This watercourse also shows a downstream increase in water discharge which is related to the size of the land area providing water to the river, i.e. the further away from the source we get, the greater the cumulative effect of water added by tributaries.

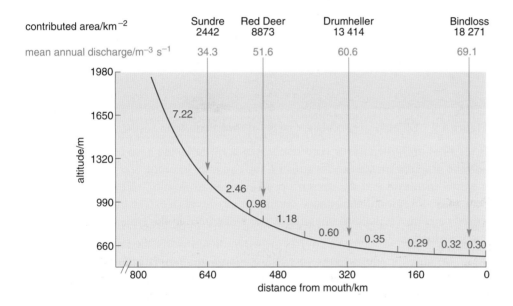

Figure 4.8   The concave upwards long profile of the Red Deer River in southern Alberta, Canada. The size of land area that contributes water to the stream, and the mean annual discharge are indicated along the top of the profile. The gradient is measured in metres per kilometre for nine sections and is indicated in red.

A graded stream is one with a concave upwards profile, which is steeper at the top and gentler at the bottom, and in which inputs and outputs of stream load are balanced. The tendency of all watercourses to become graded is related to the dynamics of fluid flow. The drag force of flowing water is related to gradient and water depth, and depth is strongly related to discharge. Expressed simply, shallow water on a steep slope can transport the same load as deep water on a shallow slope. As the discharge of a river generally increases from its source to the sea, a progressively lower gradient downstream is necessary to transport the stream load. An important feature of a graded stream is that discharge is just sufficient to transport the load provided by the drainage basin. In systems terms, inputs match outputs and the stream is in equilibrium with its surroundings.

A graded profile is strongly dependent on **base level**, the level below which a stream cannot erode (Figure 4.9). As a stream enters the sea it has no lower point to flow to and its potential energy falls to zero. An imaginary extension of sea-level beneath the land is called the **ultimate base level** of stream erosion. At this level, water has lost the ability to erode its channel. For a stream that drains into a lake, the level of the lake acts as a **local base level**. Such local base levels temporarily halt a stream's ability to erode downwards.

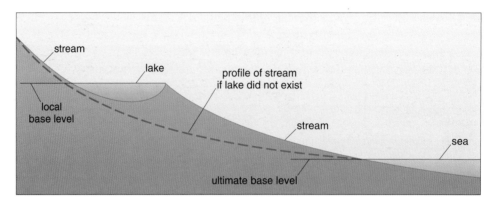

Figure 4.9   Ultimate and local base levels of stream erosion.

If regional uplift occurs, or conversely, sea-level falls, the base level is lowered and the gradient increased. As a result, the capacity to erode and transport material increases and the stream's profile becomes dominated by these processes. If regional subsidence occurs, or sea-level rises, the base level is raised causing a reduction in gradient and a decrease in the stream's ability to carry its load.

Dams effectively raise base level and reduce the gradient between the source and the dam reservoir. The decrease in slope causes a reduction in velocity upstream of the dam and material is deposited. The reservoir begins to silt up. So streams respond to a change in base level by altering how they erode and deposit material until a new grade is achieved.

4.4 Erosional landforms

4.4.1   Valleys

As soon as land is raised above sea-level, flowing water bites deep into the bedrock etching out valleys (Figure 4.10). Stream valleys are typically V-shaped in cross-section: wide at the top with a stream channel at the narrow base. The stream cuts down into the underlying rock or sediment and eventually the oversteepening of the channel sides causes collapse. This process leads to the creation of slopes on either side of the channel. As they develop, these slopes provide new sites for runoff and channel development. Over time this process leads to the development of a new drainage basin. Downcutting and therefore valley formation will decrease as the stream approaches the sea and the gradient decreases.

Figure 4.10   A 'V' shaped stream valley.

○   How do you think the shape of a stream valley is affected by rock type?

●   Where the stream cuts through resistant beds (e.g. igneous or metamorphic rocks) the valley will be narrow and steep sided. Where the stream cuts through beds less resistant to erosion (e.g. clay or shale) the valley will tend to be more broad and open. These shapes are determined by the ability of the valley slopes to resist collapse.

4.5 Depositional landforms

4.5.1   Alluvial fans

Alluvial fans are localized deposits that form where a stream loaded with sediment emerges from a confined mountain valley onto a flat unconfined plain. As the water flows out from the steep valley it spreads out and the hydraulic radius (Block 3, Part 1, Section 4.2.1) of the channel is reduced. The sudden decrease in gradient as the stream travels across the plain also causes a reduction in water speed. These factors combine to initiate the deposition of the stream's load. Alluvial fans have a semi-conical shape, with the apex of the cone pointing up the valley (Figure 4.11).

Figure 4.11   The Badwater alluvial fan in Death Valley, California, USA.

4.5.2 Floodplains

When a stream rises in flood it may overflow its banks and cover the adjacent land. The flat areas either side of the course of a stream that are naturally subject to flooding are known as **floodplains** (Figure 4.12). As the water flows out of the submerged channel, depth, speed and turbulence decrease abruptly at the channel margins. This decrease results in sudden rapid deposition of the coarser part of the suspended load (usually fine sand and silt) along the margins of the channel. Repeated flooding causes the build up of material on the edges of the channel creating banks known as natural **levées**. Farther away from the channel, finer silt and clay settle out in the quiet water.

Figure 4.12   A space radar image showing the floodplain of the Missouri River, USA. The meandering course of the Missouri River is seen as the dark curving band in the bottom half of the image. The predominantly blue area adjacent to the river is the river's floodplain.

4.5.3 Terraces

Most stream valleys contain benches or steps in the valley sides. These features are called **terraces** and are abandoned floodplains, formed when a stream became graded at a level above that of the present channel and floodplain. A change in the stream system, brought about by a drop in base level, causes a stream to erode further downwards through its deposits to a new stable level, where the next, lower, floodplain is created. This process can occur several times, each time producing a river terrace at a progressively lower level.

Most valleys have terraces and many have a number at different heights, indicating a complex history of stream evolution. If the terraces are at the same height on either side of the valley they are called paired (Figure 4.13a), if they are at different heights they are called unpaired (Figure 4.13b). Paired terraces are assumed to be the same age and are the product of periodic episodes of vertical erosion. Unpaired terraces are different in age and indicate that a stream has simply shifted from one side of the valley to the other as it was downcutting.

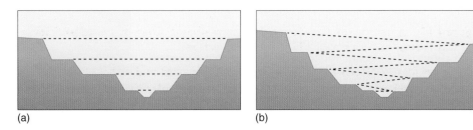

(a)   (b)

Figure 4.13   Paired (a) and unpaired (b) terraces.

○ Why is the distinction between paired and unpaired terraces important?

● Terraces are important in determining the history of the stream's evolution. Paired terraces reveal a period of deposition followed by an episode of downcutting, while unpaired terraces reflect a single episode of downcutting that simply alternated between valley sides.

downcutting?

4.5.4 Deltas

As the water of a stream meets the standing water of the sea or a lake, its speed is checked and it deposits its load to form a **delta**. The term delta was introduced in the fifth century BC by the Greek scholar Herodotus, who noted that the mouth of the River Nile has a crudely triangular shape that resembles the Greek letter Δ. As the water speed decreases the load is deposited in order of decreasing mass. The bedload is deposited first and then the suspended particles settle out. A layer representing one depositional event is typically sorted, grading from coarse sediments at the stream mouth to finer sediment offshore (Figure 4.14). Where the sea or lake bed slopes at a sharper angle than the stream channel, material is deposited on the slope to produce a foreset layer. This layer becomes thinner and finer grained further down the slope where the gradient is less, and this part of the layer is known as the bottomset layer. As more layers are deposited, the foreset layers progressively overlap the bottomset layers and the stream channel slowly migrates outwards over the extending delta. At times of high discharge, for example during floods, the top of the delta is eroded and redeposited both within and outside the channel. These deposits, which overlie the foreset layers, form a topset layer.

finer grained

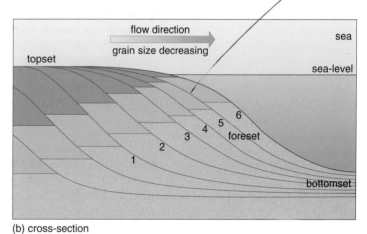

(a) plan view   (b) cross-section

Figure 4.14 A delta in (a) plan view and (b) cross-section. Coarser grained particles give way to finer grained material in a seaward direction.

During successive floods the stream channel is breached and distributary channels created, which fan out giving the delta its triangular shape (Figure 4.15).

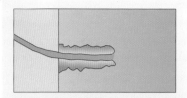
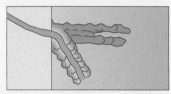
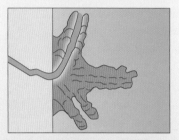
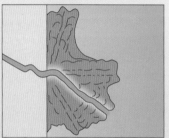
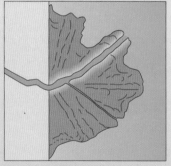

Figure 4.15   The formation of a delta by the repeated breaching of distributary channels.

Not all deltas look exactly like the model example in Figure 4.15 and different delta types can be distinguished according to their outlines.

○ What factors may be expected to affect the size and shape of a delta which builds into the sea?

● The balance between stream discharge and the power of tides and waves.

If stream discharge is high and wave and tide action relatively unimportant then the delta will build out to sea as long sand fingers to form a complex bird's foot delta (e.g. the Mississippi River Delta; Figure 4.16). This type of delta is termed a **river-dominated delta** because the main control on the delta outline is river action. If the influence of wave action is moderate then the sand fingers are reworked and smoothed out slightly to produce an arcuate form (e.g. the Nile Delta; Figure 4.17). As coastal processes become more dominant the sediment deposited by the stream is spread out in both directions along the coastline, and delta formation is inhibited. Deltas formed under these conditions may be tooth-like or 'cuspate' in plan (e.g. the Tiber Delta; Figure 4.18) and are called **wave-dominated deltas**. Although deltas are best developed where tidal range is low, they do develop in large tidal ranges. These **tide-dominated deltas** have distinctive features, such as funnel-shaped estuarine river mouths, produced by the ebb and flow of tidal currents. One example of this type of delta is the Ganges Delta (Figure 4.3) where the tides rise and fall by 4.5 m.

Figure 4.16   The Mississippi Delta. Its complex bird's foot shape is the result of a high discharge and little wave action.

Figure 4.17 The Nile Delta. Its arcuate shape is the result of moderate wave action and high discharge.

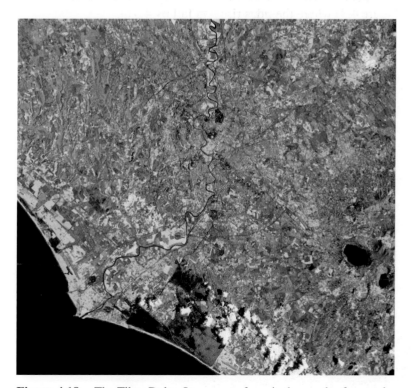

Figure 4.18 The Tiber Delta. Its cuspate form is the result of coastal processes dominating over the Tiber's discharge. Landsat 7 ETM+, copyright © ESA 2002, distributed by Eurimage.

4.6 Stream channels

One of the most obvious differences between types of stream channel is in the number and sizes of the bends and curves present. We call the measure of how straight or curved a stream is its **sinuosity** (*S*), which is expressed as follows:

$$S = \text{length of a stream channel/straight distance} \qquad (4.7)$$

Sinuosity is related to gradient. In general the steeper the gradient, the greater the degree of sinuosity. This relationship is illustrated in Figure 4.19, which reveals that, hypothetically, as gradient increases, a straight channel will transform to a sinuous channel, before eventually breaking apart into a series of short channels and bars. We will explore these different types of stream channel later.

Figure 4.19   The relationship between sinuosity, gradient and stream channel type (the terms straight, meandering and braided are explained later in the text).

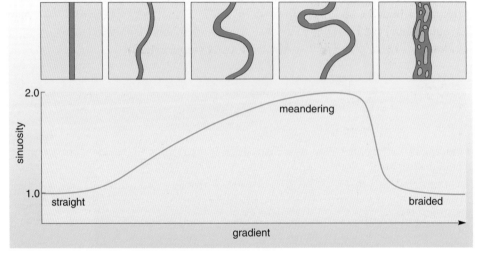

There also appears to be a relationship between sinuosity and the composition of the stream bed (Figure 4.20). Streams with a high sinuosity have a high proportion of fine-grained material (silt and clay). Streams in coarser grained, less cohesive and more easily eroded material tend to be straighter.

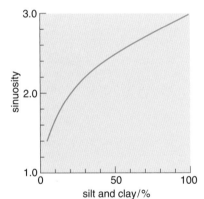

Figure 4.20   The relationship between sinuosity and bed material.

We can define three basic types of stream channel, each with a different combination of level of sinuosity and type of bank material — straight, meandering and braided. Each of the channel types blends from one to the other without an obvious division (Figure 4.21). We will now examine the different types of stream channel in more detail.

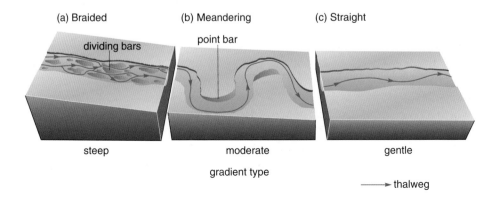

Figure 4.21   The relationships between braided, meandering and straight stream channel (these and the other terms used in the figure are explained later in the text).

4.6.1 Straight channels

Straight channels (channels with a sinuosity of < 1.5) are unusual. This type of channel is associated with gentle gradients and cohesive banks of fine silt and clay. The banks are often steep or vertical and trap the stream in a single channel. The low sinuosity reflects the absence of a significant downstream water velocity that could require energy-absorbing bends in the stream channel. However, on close inspection, even straight channels show some evidence of curves or bends. The **thalweg** (literally, *weg*, the way; *thal,* down the valley) is the line of maximum depth in a stream and usually corresponds to the line of strongest current. Even in straight channels, the thalweg usually winds from one side to the other. When it approaches one bank, sand or mud deposits usually accumulate on the opposite side, and a regular series of these bars may be found alternating from one side to the other along the channel. Straight streams also tend to have undulating beds in which shallows, called **riffles**, and deep spots, **pools**, alternate at regular intervals. So it appears that straight channels display at least some evidence of both lateral and vertical sinuosity (Figure 4.22).

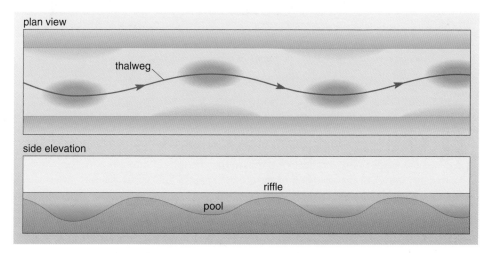

Figure 4.22 Lateral and vertical sinuosity in stream channels. The side elevation follows the path of the thalweg.

4.6.2 Meandering channels

Meandering channels (channels with a sinuosity of > 1.5) are common where the channel and floodplain have moderate gradients and cut through cohesive deposits of fine silt and clay. Compared to that carried as bedload, the amount of material transported in suspension is high in meandering streams.

The term 'meander' derives from the name of a river in Turkey fabled in ancient times for its series of bends and smooth loops that snake across the landscape. In fact, rivers usually develop a series of regular bends as they travel to larger rivers, lakes or oceans (Figure 4.23). This form of channel reflects the way in which a river minimizes resistance to flow and spreads energy as evenly as possible along its course. Most energy is dissipated in a sine-generated curve (Box 4.2). The circuitous route taken by a meandering stream represents a lessening in gradient compared to the direct path. In time, the meanders become bigger and greater in number.

Figure 4.23 A meandering stream channel with its series of regular bends.

Box 4.2 *Meanders and sine-generated curves*

A meander is not a circular curve (i.e. a series of connected semi-circles) as it has straight segments that connect the bends (Figure 4.24). Neither is it a sine or parabolic curve, i.e. a symmetrical curve that rises and falls across an axis, as the bends in the meander are too circular. In fact, a meander is a sine-generated curve (i.e. a curve that has the smallest variation in the changes of direction; for the technically-minded, the direction of the channel centre line at any point is a sine function of distance along the centre line, and a bend shape can then be generated from this function). In other words the stream does the least work in turning.

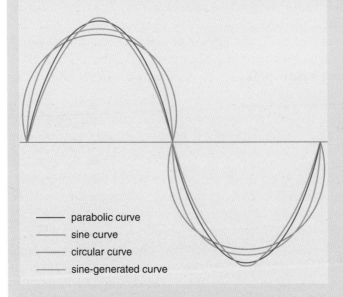

parabolic curve
sine curve
circular curve
sine-generated curve

Figure 4.24 Parabolic, sine, circular and sine-generated curves.

Imagine holding a thin strip of metal firmly at two points and bending it; the strip will avoid any concentration in bending at any one place. The strip will attempt to minimize the total work needed to accommodate the bending and will form the most uniform shape possible. So if meandering is such a fundamental phenomenon we should expect to see a similar effect elsewhere, not just in streams. In fact we do, the Gulf Stream within the Atlantic Ocean, and the atmosphere's stratospheric jet stream all display a meandering form. A catastrophic example of a sine-generated curve was provided by the crash of a Southern Railway freight train near Greenville, South Carolina, USA in 1965 (Figure 4.25). Thirty adjacent wagons carrying tightly secured 210 m sections of rail track were derailed. The violent compression that accompanied the crash folded the trainload of rails into a sine-generated curve that distributed the bending as uniformly as possible.

Figure 4.25 A catastrophic example of a sine generated curve. A Southern Railway freight train carrying tightly-secured sections of rail track derailed in South Carolina, USA in 1965. To accommodate the compression the tracks adopted a meander-like form.

Figure 4.26 A plan view and cross-section of a river meander to illustrate the helical flow of water. Water flows across the surface towards the outside of the bend and is returned by the flow across the river bed towards the inside bend. Consequently, the main current swings from one side of the channel to the other.

In a meandering stream the speed of the moving water is not the same everywhere. In a straight channel water moves the fastest in mid-channel, but as water moves around a bend, the zone of high speed swings to the outside of the channel due to centrifugal forces (Figure 4.26). The water at depth flows slower than that at the surface because of the frictional drag from the channel bed. The fast moving surface water builds up against the outside bank and generates a larger hydrostatic pressure than that caused by the slower moving water at depth. This pressure gradient causes water to sink and return to the inner bank along the river bed. This process is termed **helical flow**.

As the water moves downstream it hits each bank in turn causing erosion of the outside bend and producing cut banks. On the inside bend of the meander water is

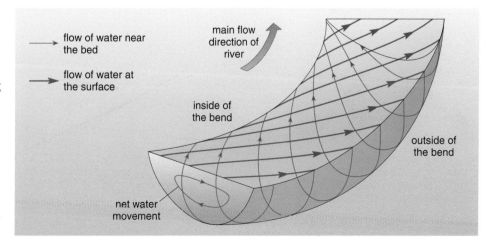

flow of water near the bed

flow of water at the surface

main flow direction of river

inside of the bend

outside of the bend

net water movement

moving more slowly and sediment is deposited to produce **point bars** (Figure 4.27). The point of maximum erosion does not occur at the mid-point of the meander, it is actually slightly downstream of the meander mid-point.

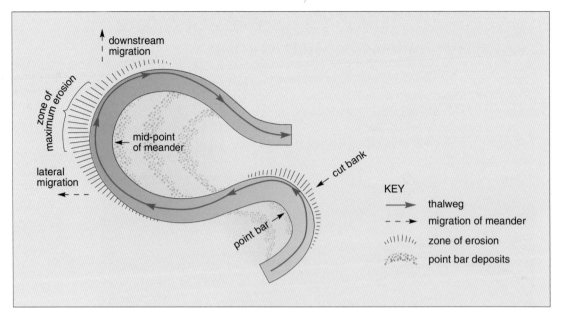

Figure 4.27   The lateral migration of a meander caused by erosion of the outside bend (cut bank) and deposition on the inside bend (point bar). Downstream migration of the meander occurs because the point of maximum erosion is slightly downstream of the meander mid-point.

○ Look again at Figure 4.27. What will be the effects of erosion on the outside and downstream portions of the meander?

● The erosion on the outside of the mid-point leads to an increase in amplitude (i.e. the meander gets wider). The erosion downstream leads to the meander migrating in that direction.

If the rate at which one meander moves downstream is greater than that of the one in front of it, then eventually only a narrow neck of land separates the two meanders. If migration continues or a period of high flow occurs, this neck can be breached leaving the old meander bend isolated. These abandoned meander bends are called **ox-bow lakes** (Figure 4.28).

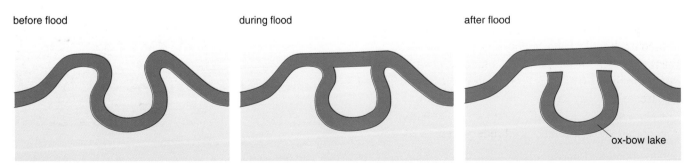

Figure 4.28   During flooding the river may breach the neck of a meander leaving the meander bend stranded. An ox-bow lake results.

○ Figure 4.29 shows part of the River Severn in mid-Wales. The floodplain sediments reveal the path of former channels. Measure the sinuosity for each period of time by laying a piece of string along the channel and comparing this to the straight line length between the two end points measured with a ruler. Has there been a change in sinuosity between 1847 and 1975?

● Sinuosity has increased from 1.71 in 1847 to 2.07 in 1975.

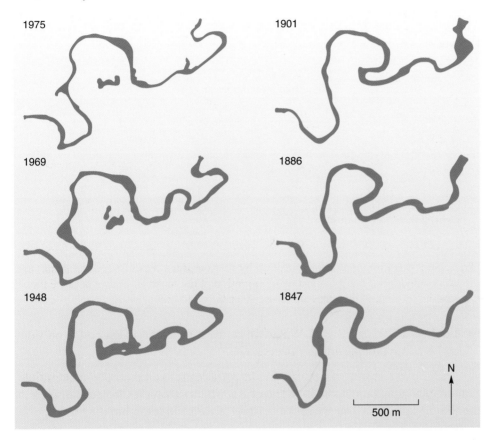

Figure 4.29 The path of the River Severn in mid-Wales between 1847 and 1975.

4.6.3 Braided channels

Braided channels are associated with steep river gradients and coarse, uncohesive bank sediments. The term 'braided' derives from the stream channel resembling interwoven strands of fabric (Figure 4.30). Braided streams occur where the stream banks are very easily eroded and where discharge is variable. During floods the stream banks are pushed back by lateral erosion. Widening the stream channel causes the stream to become shallower (i.e. the hydraulic radius becomes less), water velocity drops and the stream's ability to transport its load is diminished. Consequently, the material eroded from the banks is transported short distances and redeposited as bars.

Figure 4.30 A braided stream.

○ What effect do you think the bars will have on further deposition?

● These bars act as obstacles to water flow and grow by catching further amounts of the stream's load.

Eventually the bars build above the water surface and the stream begins to flow around the deposited material in discrete channels. Bed levels vary between different channels and water cuts across from one to the other. If fine material accumulates amongst the coarser sediments on the bars, at some point they will be stabilized by vegetation and the braided nature of the channel will be lost. It follows that the repeated destruction and reworking of the bars by floodwaters is essential to the survival of the braided stream channel.

The amount of braiding in a stream can be represented by the braiding index (Figure 4.31):

$$\text{braiding index} = \frac{\text{sum of lengths of bars in stream section}}{\text{length of stream section } (L)} \qquad (4.8)$$

Figure 4.31   Calculating the braiding index.

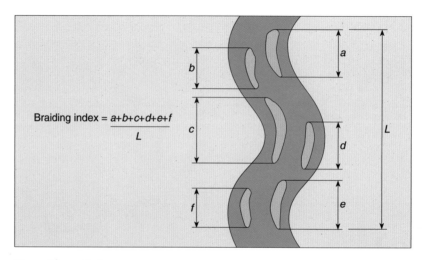

Question 4.4

Examine the graph and table in Figure 4.32, which chronicles the development of the River Platte. Can you suggest a reason for the changes in braiding index between 1885 and 1938?

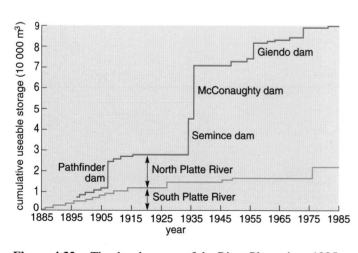

North Platte			
year	width (m)	braiding index	sinuosity index
1865	790	3.44	1.06
1938	520	1.76	1.11
1965	90		

South Platte			
year	width (m)	braiding index	sinuosity index
1867	535	2.18	1.02
1952	60	1.78	1.12
1977	91		

Figure 4.32   The development of the River Platte since 1885.

4.6.4 Stream channels and their environments

So different stream channels occur under different environmental conditions. Table 4.4 is a summary of the conditions in which each of the three channel types are found when discharge is assumed to be constant.

Table 4.4 Stream channels and their ideal environments.

Bank material	Gradient		
	low	medium	high
cohesive (fine grained)	straight	meander	–
uncohesive (coarse grained)	–	–	braided

○ If a meandering stream suddenly became a braided stream what change in environmental conditions could have occurred?

● The local gradient may have increased or the bank materials of the floodplain may have become incoherent. See Box 4.3 for an assessment of these two possible processes in a past environment.

Box 4.3 Stream channels and the end Permian mass extinction

Around 250 Ma ago, at the end of the Permian period, the Earth suffered its biggest recorded mass extinction. The cause of the mass extinction is still hotly debated but it is certain that ecosystems on land and in the sea suffered greatly. One valuable clue to the ecosystem collapse on land is present in the Permian rocks of the Karoo Basin of South Africa where geological evidence reveals a rapid, basin-wide change from meandering to braided stream channels. For a number of years it was believed that a widespread increase in gradient occurred, but due to geological evidence this has been recently dismissed. The braiding, therefore, must have resulted from a decrease in the strength of channel bank sediments and an increase in stream load. It seems that as plant life on land perished their roots could no longer bind the sediments, allowing them to be washed away.

In Figure 4.33 you can see Permian sediments once again on the move. The steep sea cliffs near Teignmouth, Devon, UK are made up of Permian sandstones and the small channels of water that drain from them display a braided form due to their high stream load and uncohesive, sandy bank sediments. This present-day stream channel gives us an idea of the processes operating 250 Ma ago, albeit on a much smaller scale.

Figure 4.33 Braiding in small channels of water near Teignmouth, Devon, UK.

Question 4.5

Assume that the lake in Figure 4.9 contains 5 000 000 kg of water and lies at an altitude of 4000 m. Calculate the potential energy for this water mass.

Question 4.6

Consider a situation in which a stream is dammed both upstream and downstream of a location that you have begun to study. What will happen to the various types of stream load as the stream section dries out?

Question 4.7

Look at the drainage basin in Figure 4.5. What type of stream pattern does it show? Does this suggest a young or old drainage surface? What are the bifurcation ratios for the various stream orders?

Question 4.8

Over time, the braiding index of a stream channel decreases and its sinuosity becomes greater. Is this change consistent with an increase or decrease in gradient? Assume that stream load measurements for this stream reveal that the load furnished by the stream's drainage basin is greater than that carried out of the basin by the stream. Would you consider this a graded stream?

4.7 Summary of Section 4

1   Fluvial processes are driven by the potential energy of water, evaporated from the sea and precipitated at higher elevations. Gravity encourages the water to flow down to sea-level, eroding material on the way.

2   Some water flows in channels to form streams, and turbulent flow aids the erosion of material.

3   Material transported by streams can be divided into three fractions: dissolved load, suspended load and bedload.

4   Eventually a stream becomes graded and achieves equilibrium with its environment. It develops a concave upwards long profile and has sufficient discharge to transport the load furnished by the drainage basin.

5   Erosional features, such as valleys, indicate that material is being removed locally by fluvial processes, whilst depositional features, such as alluvial fans, floodplains and deltas indicate that material is being added locally.

6   Different gradients, discharge regimes and bank materials produce different types of stream channel. The extent to which a stream is straight, meandering or braided can be determined by calculating the sinuosity and braiding index.

Learning outcomes for Section 4

Now that you have completed your study of Section 4 you should be able to:

4.1 Explain the role of potential energy in fluvial processes. (*Question 4.5*)

4.2 Describe the different types of load found in streams. (*Question 4.6*)

4.3 Outline how we 'measure' the streams in a drainage basin. (*Questions 4.1, 4.2, 4.3 and 4.7*)

4.4 Recognize different stream patterns. (*Question 4.7*)

4.5 Explain how, when given enough time, a stream achieves equilibrium with its surroundings by becoming graded. (*Question 4.8*)

4.6 Distinguish between erosional and depositional fluvial landforms.

4.7 Recognize different types of stream channel. (*Question 4.8*)

5

Water: coastal landforms

Where the ocean meets the land, there is a tumultuous, energetic zone of activity. Sediment is deposited into the sea by in-flowing rivers while waves that have travelled many kilometres across the open ocean erode and re-work the shoreline (Figure 5.1).

Figure 5.1 The Old Man of Hoy, UK. A dramatic product of coastal processes.

5.1 Waves

5.1.1 How waves are formed

The landforms we observe along coasts are predominantly shaped by ocean waves. Waves are generated by winds that blow across the surface of the sea: the friction between the air and water transfers energy from the atmosphere to the ocean.

Contrary to popular belief, waves do not involve any significant transport of water; they merely transfer a disturbance in one part of the water to another, a movement of energy. For example, a boat floating at sea merely bobs up and down in the water without moving in the direction of the waves. The motion of a wave is similar to that seen when the wind blows across a field of tall grass, the grass stalks bend forward before returning to their original position. An ocean wave is similar in that the water moves forward, but dissimilar in that the return leg occurs at a lower elevation, before being raised and pushed forward again. The result is that each parcel of water moves in a loop-like or oscillating motion (Figure 5.2).

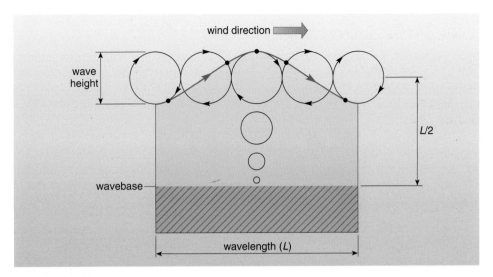

Figure 5.2 The measurable characteristics and loop-like motion of waves.

The oscillating circulation of water particles in waves occurs on different scales; the main factors that determine the size of a wave are how long and fast the wind blows. If the wind that generates waves is fast and constant, the wave height will increase for as long as the wind blows. The distance of open water across which the wind has blown is known as the **fetch**. For a long fetch, the height of a wave is related to wind speed. So, the greater the fetch and wind speed, the larger the wave and also the more energy it possesses.

The energy a wave contains includes a certain amount of potential energy, as a result of its height, as well as some kinetic energy due to the motion of the water within the wave.

5.1.2 The nature of waves

There are several characteristics of waves that can be measured (Figure 5.2). **Wavelength** is the horizontal distance between the highest points of the waves (the wave crests) or, alternatively, between the lowest points of the waves (the wave troughs). **Wave height** is the vertical difference between the wave trough and its crest. The time taken for successive crests to pass a point is called the **wave period**. The wavelength is equal to the speed of the wave multiplied by the wave period:

$$L = \text{speed} \times \text{period} \tag{5.1}$$

Where L is wavelength.

The diameters of the loops of water particles at the water surface exactly equal wave height. At increasing depths there is a progressive loss of energy and the diameters of the loops diminish. At a depth equal to half the wavelength ($L/2$) the diameters of the loops are negligible.

○   How do you think a depth corresponding to $L/2$ is important for wave erosion?

●   As the depth $L/2$ is the lower limit of the looping motion of wave particles it is also the lower limit of wave erosion, the **wavebase**.

In theory, erosion by waves could ultimately reduce the Earth's landmasses to a planed-off surface at this level. In the Pacific Ocean, wavelengths of 600 m have been measured, which give a $L/2$ of 300 m. This depth is much greater than the average depth of the sea floor adjacent to the continents and suggests that waves can be important erosive agents. However, most waves have wavelengths much less than 600 m.

When a wave travelling towards land reaches a depth of water equal to $L/2$, its base meets the bottom and the form of the wave changes (Figure 5.3). Due to friction on the sea-bed, the loop-like motion becomes elliptical, the wave height increases quickly and the wavelength decreases rapidly; often the height of the wave is doubled.

As the front of the wave approaches shallower water it becomes steeper than the rear. With progression landwards the steepening continues until the wave becomes unsustainable and collapses or breaks.

5.1.3 The energy of waves

When a wave breaks, turbulence is created and **surf** is observed (Figure 5.4). As the wave breaks, its potential energy is converted into kinetic energy, providing a large amount of energy for the wave to do work along the shoreline. In the turbulent surf, each wave smashes against rock or rushes up the beach as **swash** until its kinetic energy is dispersed. Then it flows back as **backwash**, which may be in the form of broad sheets (**undertow**) or narrow channels (**rip currents**). Surf contains most of the energy of the original wave. This energy is consumed in turbulence, friction on the bed and violent sediment movement. Most of the work of waves is performed by surf, landward of the line of breaking waves (Figure 5.3).

At what depth of water can surf erode and transport sediment? Well this depends on the depth at which waves break. Most waves break when water depth has decreased to 1.5 times their wave height. Waves are rarely more than 6 m high, so erosion is theoretically limited to 1.5×6 m, or 9 m. Hence, in theory, the surf zone is limited to an area that extends from the **shoreline** to 9 m water depth.

Figure 5.3   The changing characteristics of waves as they approach the shore.

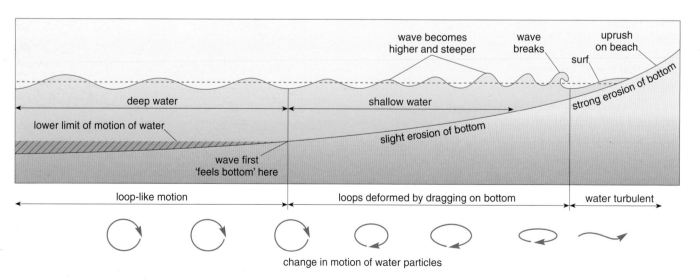

change in motion of water particles

Figure 5.4 The surf from a breaking wave.

5.1.4 Constructive and destructive waves

When a wave of low height to wavelength ratio (less than 0.025) travels towards a beach, the wave steepens gradually and tends to break gently or spill on the beach. As these waves move up the beach they rapidly lose energy and tend to percolate into the beach material and, therefore, the subsequent backwash has little energy to remove sediment offshore from the beach. These waves are called constructive waves and are important in building up beaches, because they push more material up the beach than they remove from it.

High waves with height to wavelength ratios of approximately 0.25 or more, steepen sharply as they progress landward and tend to plunge onto the beach, stirring the sediment violently and transporting it offshore in powerful backwash. These waves are called destructive waves and they withdraw sediment from beaches.

5.1.5 Refracted waves

When a wave approaches a straight shore at an oblique angle not all the wave hits the shallow sea floor at the same time. The drag of the sea floor slows that part of the wave which is closest to the shore. The net effect of this process is that the wave gradually swings round to break nearly parallel to the shore (Figure 5.5).

Figure 5.5 The crests of waves that approach the shore at an angle curve as they reach shallower water, so that they reach the beach almost parallel to the shoreline.

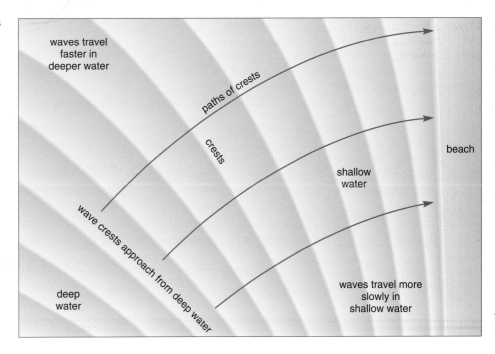

waves travel faster in deeper water

paths of crests

crests

shallow water

beach

wave crests approach from deep water

deep water

waves travel more slowly in shallow water

This process is known as **wave refraction**. Where waves encounter a protrusion in the coastline, such as a headland, wave refraction over the shallower water offshore causes the waves to turn in, and their energy converges on the front and sides of the protrusion (Figure 5.6).

○ If headlands are the focus of wave energy what happens in bays?

● Waves approaching a bay are refracted outwards and their energy is dispersed to the sides of the bay.

Figure 5.6 As a result of refraction, wave energy is concentrated on headlands, where erosion is dominant, and dispersed in bays, where deposition occurs.

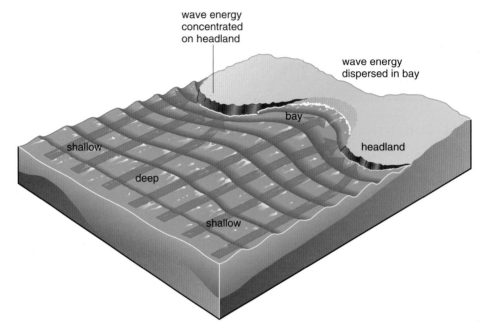

Due to wave refraction, headlands are sites of intense erosion, whereas bays are areas of deposition. This is why bays are often filled with sandy beaches. Over time, wave refraction causes irregularities in the coastline to be smoothed out.

5.2 Tides

5.2.1 How tides are formed

Roughly every 12 hours there are rises and falls in sea-level, known as the **tides**, which result from the gravitational pull of the Moon and Sun.

Imagine an Earth completely covered with water (Figure 5.7). The ocean on the side of the Earth facing the Moon is attracted by its gravitational pull. This creates a **tidal bulge** on the side of the Earth facing the Moon. As the Earth rotates, the tidal bulge is dragged around the globe and hits the continents regularly.

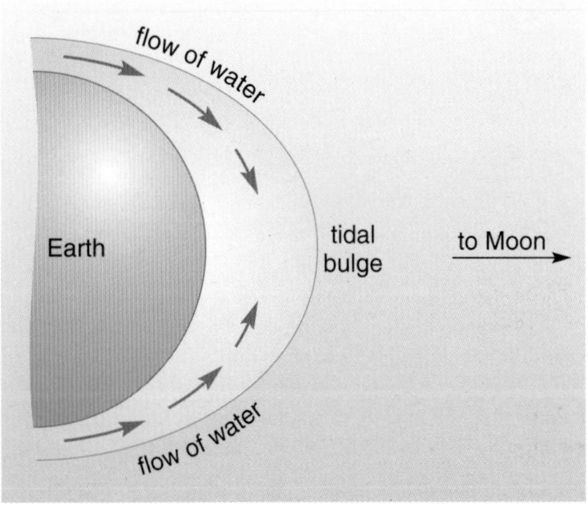

Figure 5.7 The formation of tidal bulges.

5.2.2 The effect of tides

The difference between high and low tide levels is called the **tidal range**. A low tidal range means that the effect of breaking waves is limited to a narrow band of the shore. A high tidal range means that the force of the waves is spread over a much greater distance and is, therefore, locally less effective. You can visualize this effect with the help of a simple analogy. The force of water coming from a garden hose is quite gentle when dispersed widely through a spray, but much more powerful when narrowly focused through a nozzle.

In the open sea the effects of tides are minor, but in narrow coastal inlets tides can generate rapid currents which redistribute fine sediments within bays and estuaries. These tidal currents can also be effective in moving eroded material. While incoming and outgoing tides produce currents in opposite directions on a daily basis, the current in one direction is usually stronger than in the other, resulting in a net one-way transport of sediment.

5.3 Coastal processes

5.3.1 Coastal erosion

The erosive processes that dominate on shorelines involve a significant amount of physical weathering. The main erosive agent is wave action; the impact of tons of water against solid rock pummels solid cliffs into fragments. Wave action is aided by abrasion, hydraulic action and cavitation (Section 2.2.1). The chemical weathering that occurs when seawater is forced into small cracks and crevices enhances the destructive power of the waves. Fissures are extended and widened, eventually becoming susceptible to the erosive power of wave action. The removal of materials by wave and tide action can produce spectacular erosional features along a coastline (Figure 5.8).

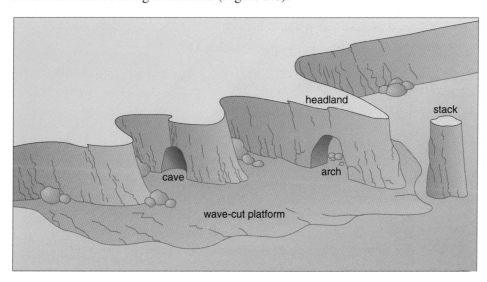

Figure 5.8 Coastal erosional features.

One of the dramatic products of coastal erosion is the cliff. Cliffs are steep land surfaces that extend down to the sea — the result of erosion at sea-level and the subsequent collapse of the rocks above (Figure 5.9).

Figure 5.9 The chalk cliffs of the Seven Sisters, Sussex, UK.

○ In what way will the energy of the waves affect the rates of erosion and the landforms produced?

● When cliffs are pounded by energetic waves, erosion rates are high and steep rock faces are produced. Smaller, gentler sloping scarps are usually the result of gentler wave action.

○ Consider some of the coastlines you have visited. Do you think wave energy is the only controlling factor on erosion rates?

● No. The rock type which makes up a cliff face is also important. Granite, for instance, is less easily eroded than volcanic ash (Table 5.1).

○ Look again at Table 5.1. If wave energy was constant, which cliff materials would give the steepest and gentlest cliff faces?

● Granite would give the steepest cliff face because it is a hard rock and would resist collapse. Volcanic ash would give the gentlest cliff face because it is a soft material that would collapse relatively easily.

Table 5.1 Rates of cliff erosion for different rock types.

Cliff material	Rate of cliff erosion/yr
granite	1 mm
limestone	1 mm–1 cm
shale	1 cm
chalk	10 cm
glacial drift	1–10 m
volcanic ash	10 m

At the base of a cliff there may be a flat, bench-like surface — a wave-cut platform. Erosion by the sea cuts a notch into the cliff base and, as erosion proceeds, this notch deepens leading to the collapse of the cliff face above. The debris from the collapse is washed back and forth by the sea, abrading the bedrock at sea-level. Landward progression of this process produces a polished horizontal platform (Figure 5.10). Uplift of the land or a drop in sea-level can leave these wave-cut platforms exposed as obvious 'raised beaches'.

Because wave erosion is not uniform along a coast and attacks various rock types at different rates, dramatic features such as stacks and arches can develop. Rocks that have vertical joints or fissures are particularly susceptible to selective erosion. Wave attack on the sides of a headland can sometimes lead to the formation of caves, which may be eroded right through the headland so a natural

Figure 5.10 A wave-cut platform at Elie, Fife, UK.

arch is developed. This process has created the arch known as the Green Bridge of Wales (Figure 5.11). Eventually, the roof of the arch becomes unstable and collapses to leave an isolated stack. Good examples of such stacks are the Needles on the Isle of Wight, UK (Figure 5.12).

Figure 5.11 The Green Bridge of Wales, a natural arch in Pembrokeshire, UK.

Figure 5.12 The Needles, sea stacks on the Isle of Wight, UK.

5.3.2   Coastal transport

Although wave refraction tends to turn oncoming waves parallel to the shoreline, most waves strike the shore at an oblique angle. When oblique-angled waves hit a shoreline they are refracted and generate a **longshore current**, which flows parallel to the shore and carries beach material with it. Because waves strike the beach at an angle, the swash of the wave travels obliquely up the beach, but the backwash flows straight down the beach. The result is **beach drift**, a zigzag movement of sand and pebbles along the shore. Drift resulting from the longshore current and beach drift is called **longshore drift** (Figure 5.13).

Figure 5.13   Two processes that generate longshore drift. (a) Beach drift, the zigzag movement of material by swash and backwash. (b) Longshore current is generated by the arrival of oblique-angled waves and is a powerful mover of underwater beach material.

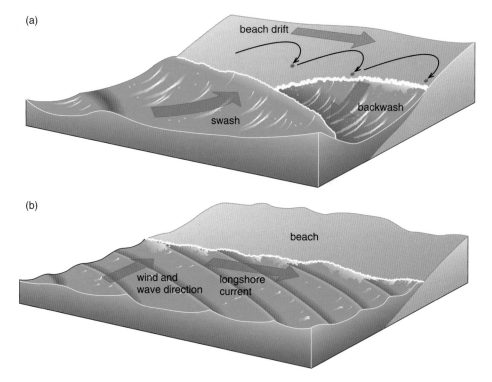

5.3.3   Coastal deposition

The best known and most common depositional landform on coastlines is the beach. Around 40% of the world's coastlines have beaches that consist of thick, wedge-shaped accumulations of unconsolidated sand and gravel. Beach materials can originate from several sources. Some material can be washed down to the coast by rivers while some is derived from the erosion of the coastline itself. Material can also be washed from the sea floor by waves and currents or be blown in from the nearby land by wind.

The sediment transported by longshore drift can produce depositional features along a coastline (Figure 5.14).

Spits are elongate ridges of material that project from land and end in the open sea (Figure 5.15). These spits are essentially extensions of beaches, created by longshore drift. The free end of the spit curves towards the land in response to currents generated by the surf.

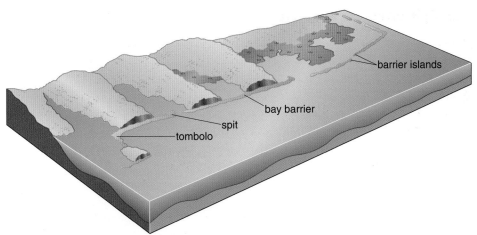

Figure 5.14 Depositional landforms found along coasts.

If a lack of strong tidal or river currents allow a spit to extend completely across a bay it becomes a **bay barrier** (Figure 5.14). **Tombolos** are similar to spits and bay barriers in that they are ridges of beach material, but rather than end in the open sea or block a bay they connect one island to another or to the mainland (Figure 5.16). **Barrier islands** are long islands of sediment, which lie offshore and parallel to the coast. Some barrier islands are formed by the longshore growth of spits while others are the result of the emergence of an offshore bar during sea-level lowering or the submergence of a coastal sand ridge during sea-level rise.

Figure 5.15 Spurn Head, a spit, Yorkshire, UK.

Figure 5.16 Chesil Beach, a tombolo, Dorset, UK.

5.4 The beach budget

The balance between erosion and deposition of material on a beach can be assessed by drawing up a beach budget. Inputs of material to a beach come from several sources, including sand from longshore drift, sand washed onshore from the sea floor, sand from the hinterland cliffs and dunes, and river-transported sand (Figure 5.17). Outputs include sand lost by longshore drift, sand lost offshore to the sea floor, sand blown inland, sand lost through *in situ* weathering and sand swept upstream into an estuary or inlet. As the term implies, a beach budget is used to determine whether a beach is showing a net loss or gain in volume, and requires data from repeated surveys on a particular area. Beach profiles are monitored and aerial photographs taken for a section of the coastline. Specific compartments of certain width, height and depth are defined to enable cross-section volumes to be calculated. Once this has been done, alongshore comparisons are made to discover the parts of a beach that are shrinking or growing in size.

(a) Supply of sand to a beach

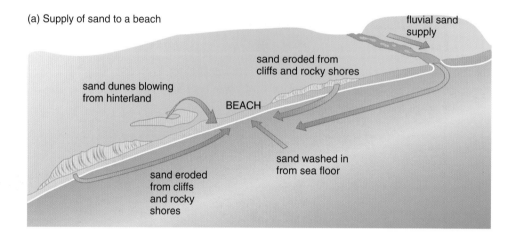

(b) Losses of sand from a beach

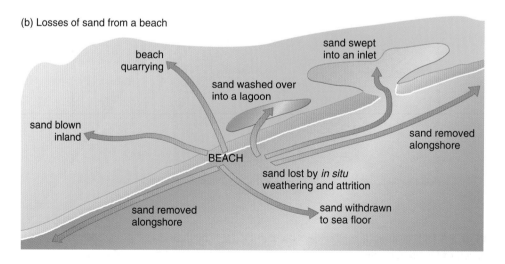

Figure 5.17   The inputs (a) and outputs (b) of the beach budget.

When investigating the causes of net increase or decrease in beach volume identified by the beach budget, it is useful to be able to trace the flow of beach sediments along a coastline. The accretion of material is not always due to longshore drift, as contributions can be washed in from the sea floor. One obvious way to identify the processes that are operating is to track the transport of unusual rock types which are specific to a particular part of the coastline. A more ambitious proposal is to use variations in the brightness or 'luminescence' of quartz to reveal sediment flow.

An example of how a beach budget can reveal changes in the environment is provided by the barrier beach that protects the coast of North Carolina, USA. In 1933 a hurricane passed just south of Ocean City and breached the barrier to form an inlet known today as Ocean City Inlet, which now separates Assateague Island from Ocean City to the north. In Figure 5.18, traditional beach survey methods have been supplemented by creating continuous digital elevation maps of the area using airborne laser beach mapping.

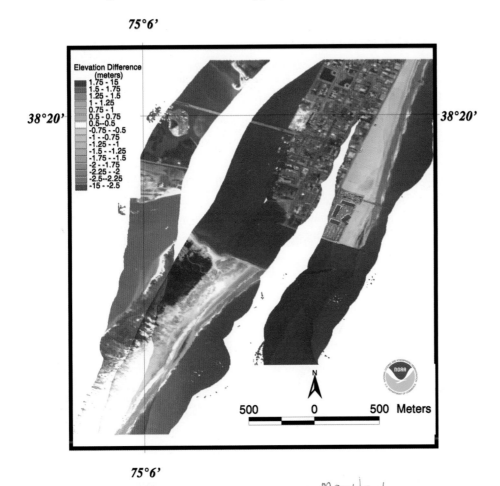

Figure 5.18   A map of the barrier beach at Ocean City, ~~North Carolina~~ Maryland, USA. The wide beach of Ocean City lies north of the Ocean City inlet. The narrower beach of Assateague Island lies to the south. The data were compiled between 1997 and 2000, from a laser altimeter, the NASA Airborne Topographic Mapper. Differences in elevation during this time period are represented by the following colours: not coloured, no change; green, elevation increase; yellow/red, elevation decrease.

Ocean City Inlet quickly became a popular navigation channel, and rock jetties extending over 150 m seaward on both the north and south sides of the inlet were built to preserve it. The construction of the jetty led to an immediate disruption of the natural north to south drift of beach material and changed the erosion and deposition rates north and south of the inlet. Near Ocean City, north of the rock jetty, a wide sand beach developed. On Assateague Island, south of the rock jetty, the beach began to erode at an increasing rate.

The beach budget of Assateague Island can be described as a system with the following components:

C_s the amount of sand present in a cross-section of the barrier beach at the start of a time period

C_f the amount of sand present in this cross-section when the time period has finished

A_d the sand added by longshore drift

A_w the sand added by the wind

R_d the sand removed by longshore drift

R_w the sand removed into the tidal marshes or lagoons by the wind or by flooding.

These components are related by the equation:

$$C_f = C_s + A_d + A_w - R_d - R_w \tag{5.2}$$

The beach budget balances when:

$$A_d + A_w = R_d + R_w \tag{5.3}$$

As the introduction of material to the beach will, inevitably, cause it to build out to sea, the shoreline advances when the balance is positive, i.e. $C_f > C_s$. Conversely, the removal of material from the beach will lead to a negative balance ($C_f < C_s$) and a receding shoreline.

●   Would you expect C_f or C_s to be greater near Ocean City, north of the rock jetty?

○ C_f would be greater as the amount of sand has increased due to the trapping effect of the rock jetty.

●   Will the accumulation of beach material north of the rock jetty continue indefinitely?

○   No. At some point the beach will have built out to the seaward edge of the rock jetty. After this point the advance of the shoreline near Ocean City will cease and material will be transported across the inlet and southward along the coast.

Question 5.1

When the beach near Ocean City has built out past the rock jetty and material is once again transported southward along the coast, the relationships between A_d and R_d on Assateague Island will change. Describe how.

Disturbance in the beach budget leads to the advance or retreat of the shoreline. For human settlements near the sea, shoreline retreat can be a major problem, as storms and high waves may more easily destroy towns and villages. Occasionally, beach material is extracted for industrial purposes and in these situations careful monitoring of the beach budget is crucial to avoid such catastrophes. Box 5.1 describes one episode where the importance of the beach budget was underestimated.

Box 5.1 The vanishing village of Hallsands

One example of how disturbance to the beach budget can have catastrophic consequences is provided by the story of Hallsands, Start Bay, Devon, UK. This 'romantic hamlet' was once a secure home to a fishing community of over 100 people. The village was established in the 16th century on a site protected from the sea by a shingle ridge (Figure 5.19a). At the turn of the 20th century shingle was removed from the bay to make concrete for nearby docks. The shingle had protected Hallsands from the tides — and without it the cottages were demolished by a storm (Figure 5.19b).

The Exeter Express and Echo newspaper reported the destruction in its Monday, 29 January, 1917 edition:

Not within living memory has there been such a terrible visitation of the South Devon coast as was experienced on Friday and Saturday when a furious south-east gale raged for several hours, and, combined with an abnormally high tide which rose some four or five feet above the maximum, wrought havoc at Torcross, Hallsands and other places. … At one time there was a fine shingle beach here which acted as a kind of barrier, but large quantities of the shingle was removed some years ago for constructing concrete blocks for Keyham Extension Works. … When morning broke a scene of desolation presented itself to the eye. The fishing boats had been tossed up clean into the meadow, wreckage was strewn about in all directions and the village practically wiped out. The seas swamped right over the houses, which seemed to crumple beneath their weight. Some of the people had a terrible experience. In one case there were nine people huddled together in a little house against which the waves were incessantly dashing, and they were expecting every moment that the walls which afforded them shelter would collapse, and they would be washed away. They had to bore holes in the bedroom floor to let the water down into the kitchen. … One old fisherman sorrowfully viewing the wreckage on Saturday said 'This is the end of our village. We shall have to go elsewhere'.

(a)

(b)

Figure 5.19 The village of Hallsands, (a) before, and (b) after it was left vulnerable and finally destroyed by a storm following the extraction of shingle from the bay.

Question 5.2

Rewrite the beach budget equation to reflect the possibility of negative and positive influences of human activity at Hallsands.

Question 5.3

A wave has a wave height of 1 m and a wavelength of 3 m. Calculate whether this wave is likely to add or remove material from a beach.

Question 5.4

Is the Old Man of Hoy in Figure 5.1 an erosional or depositional landform? Outline the sequence of events that led to its formation.

5.5 Summary of Section 5

1   Coastal landforms are predominantly shaped by ocean waves.
2   The height of a wave is determined by the fetch and wind speed.
3   Depending on the height and wavelength, a wave may be constructive and build up a beach, or destructive and remove material from a beach.
4   Wave refraction concentrates wave energy on headlands and other protrusions and tends to remove irregularities in the coastline.
5   Wave action erodes material from the coastline and transports it along the beach by longshore drift.
6   The balance between inputs and outputs of material on a beach is reflected in the beach budget.

Learning outcomes for Section 5

Now that you have completed your study of Section 5 you should be able to:

5.1   Explain how waves and tides are formed.
5.2   Describe how waves affect the coastline. (*Questions 5.1, 5.2, 5.3 and 5.4*)
5.3   Distinguish between erosional and depositional coastal landforms. (*Questions 5.1, 5.2 and 5.4*)
5.4   Recognize that beaches are systems with inputs and outputs of material. (*Questions 5.1 and 5.2*)

Ice

6

Bodies of ice are major repositories of the Earth's fresh water. If all the ice on the land were to melt and flow into the oceans, world sea-level would rise by approximately 70 m. Stores of ice are important for fluvial systems, as almost all the world's major rivers have their origins at altitude, in icy mountain basins. Over time ice bodies expand and shrink, responding to changes in the environment, and by monitoring the nature of the Earth's ice stores we can compile valuable records of environmental change. Later in the course you will deal with the Earth's frozen water in detail when you study Block 5. Here we will briefly look at the common types of ice bodies found on the Earth and how they sculpt the land.

6.1 Glaciers

Glaciers are like rivers of ice that move gradually downhill. They are an integral part of the water cycle, albeit one which appears to be moving in slow motion. For a body of ice to be called a glacier it must persist on the land throughout the year and have, or have had in the past, the ability to flow (Figure 6.1). Today ice covers $9.5 \times 10^6 \, \text{km}^2$ or approximately 10% of the Earth's surface and, except for Australia, glaciers exist on every continent. Glaciers are produced by snowfall and low temperatures, and these conditions are found in two areas: mountains and polar regions. Discounting sea ice, glaciers can be divided into two main groups: **ice sheets** and **ice caps**, and **valley glaciers**.

Figure 6.1   The Gilkey Glacier, Alaska, USA.

6.1.1 Ice sheets and caps

Ice in polar regions occurs as vast continent-sized ice sheets that smother almost all of the land surface within their perimeter. At the present day these ice sheets occur in Greenland (3.6×10^6 km^3; Figure 6.2) and Antarctica (27×10^6 km^3; Figure 6.3) and, together, comprise 95% of the ice of the planet. Smaller ice sheets, which cover mountain highlands or lower lying lands at high latitudes, are called ice caps and are hundreds of cubic kilometres in volume. The relatively small Quelccaya Ice Cap in the Peruvian Andes covers 70 km^2 and lies at an altitude of 4950–5645 m. The Vatnajökull ice cap in Iceland is much larger at about 14 000 km^2, and reaches sea-level (Figure 6.4).

Figure 6.2 The southern tip of the Greenland Ice Sheet. **Figure 6.3** The Antarctic Ice Sheet, Antarctica.

Figure 6.4 The Vatnajökull Ice Cap, Iceland.

6.1.2 Valley glaciers

Glaciers in mountain regions are termed valley glaciers. They are ribbons of ice confined by the surrounding topography, which controls their shape and direction of movement (Figure 6.5). Small alpine glaciers occupy hollows or depressions in the sides of mountains, while larger alpine glaciers spread downwards onto valley floors and lowlands and may coalesce to form intermontane (literally 'between mountain ranges') icefields. Most of the world's valley glaciers are no more than about 1–2 km long and have areas less than several square kilometres. Some large valley glaciers in Alaska and Asia are tens of kilometres long.

Figure 6.5 A valley glacier, the Gornergrat Glacier, Swiss Alps.

○ Do you think valley glaciers and ice sheets could ever exist together?

● Continental ice sheets divide into narrow tongues of ice at their periphery. These tongues act in the same way as alpine glaciers.

6.2 Glacial processes

6.2.1 Properties of ice

Fresh snow is a mass of delicate ice crystals with a density around 5–30% that of water (50–300 kg m^{-3}), and is very porous. As the snow ages on the ground, air penetrates the pore spaces initiating cycles of sublimation (i.e. when ice is directly changed into water vapour) and refreezing. The original snowflakes are transformed into small round crystals (Figure 6.6). This partly melted, compressed snow is called **névé**. Névé has a higher density than fresh snow, exceeding 500 kg m^{-3}. After about a year, the fall of fresh snow has compacted the névé further into a yet denser form called **firn**, with fewer pore spaces. Further burial and compaction transforms firn into glacial ice, which has a density of about 850 kg m^{-3}. Overall, the transformation of freshly fallen snow into (glacial) ice may take 25 to 100 years.

snowflakes
round crystal = névé
these compact under
more snowfall
FIRN
+ compaction burial
GLACIAL ICE

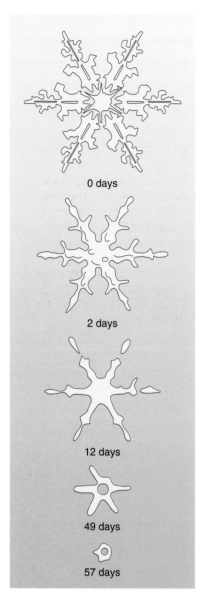

0 days

2 days

12 days

49 days

57 days

Figure 6.6 The formation of névé from snow.

6.2.2 Glacier movement

When ice on a slope builds to a great enough thickness it will begin to deform and flow downslope under the pull of gravity. The effect of thickness on flow can be illustrated by analogy with a viscous fluid such as honey. A thin layer of honey on a slightly tilted tray flows very slowly. But pour more honey on the tray and it begins to flow more rapidly. Tilt the tray more and it flows faster still. So the greater the thickness of glacial ice and the steeper the gradient, the faster the flow.

Part of this flow is accomplished through movement within individual ice crystals. As the pressure of snow accumulating on the glacier increases, higher stress is placed on the glacial ice and deformation or creep takes place along internal planes within individual ice crystals. This deformation occurs in much the same way as the playing cards in a deck slide over one another as the deck is pushed from one end.

○ How can small movements in ice crystals (about a ten millionth of a millimetre) affect a large glacier?

● The sum total of these small movements in an enormous number of ice crystals over long time periods amounts to much larger movements of the whole glacial mass.

Other processes are also at work within the ice. Ice crystals tend to melt and then recrystallize a small distance downslope, and over time crystals tend to orientate themselves in a downslope direction, which favours further flow.

The remaining flow is achieved in some glaciers through sliding along the glacier base. Dry-based glaciers are cold glaciers that are frozen to the ground beneath, and in these circumstances internal deformation is the major process. Wet-based glaciers have ice at their base that is at its melting point, and repeated melting and freezing at the glacier base helps the glacier to slide downslope.

○ Can you suggest how melting occurs at the base of an object as cold as a glacier?

● The melting is brought about due to a combination of overlying ice pressure and the heat emanating upwards from the interior of the Earth.

A common demonstration of how pressure can melt ice involves hanging a wire, weighted at both ends, over a block of ice. The wire gradually passes through the block as the ice underneath it melts under pressure. Once the wire has passed through any particular part of the ice block the pressure is removed and the ice refreezes. Eventually the wire passes through the ice block and falls to the floor leaving a solid block of ice behind. In some glaciers, this type of pressure melting means that basal sliding can account for 90% of the total flow.

6.2.3 Rates of flow

Traditionally the surface speed of a valley glacier has been measured by placing markers in the ice and observing their changes in position over a few years. These types of studies show that ice in the centre of the glacier moves faster than that at the sides (Figure 6.7). The reduced speed of the edges of the glacier is due to frictional drag at the valley sides. A similar reduction in speed occurs towards the base of the glacier, and this can be observed by drilling a borehole through the glacier and repeatedly measuring the angle of the hole at different depths over time. Today, these types of studies are performed using remote sensing techniques but the conclusions remain the same, ice at the centre and surface of a glacier moves faster that that at the sides and base, a similar velocity distribution to that seen in rivers. Rates of flow can vary from 10–200 m yr^{-1} (Figure 6.7).

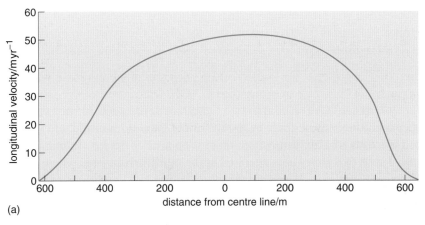

(a)

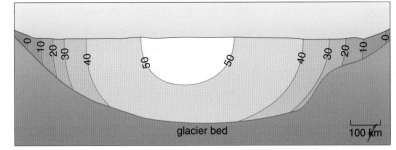

(b)

Figure 6.7 The rates of flow in glaciers. (a) A graph showing the downslope velocity of ice at different points on a glacier's surface. Velocity is highest at the centre of the glacier's surface and decreases towards its sides. (b) Cross-section of a glacier showing its downslope velocity distribution (m yr^{-1}). Velocity decreases towards the base and sides.

6.3 Mass balance

Glaciers can be viewed as systems that are influenced by a number of inputs and outputs.

○ What do you think is the main input to a glacier?

● Snow, which over time is converted to glacial ice.

○ What do you think is the main output from a glacier?

● The main output from the system is meltwater created when the ice melts, or escaping vapour created when it sublimes.

○ Consider a single point in the centre of the glacier. What other process will be introducing and removing mass?

● Locally, the flow of the glacier will be introducing and removing ice to and from this point.

The mass of a glacier is constantly changing as environmental conditions change on both short and long time-scales. Environmental changes cause fluctuations in the amount of snow input to the glacier system and the amount of snow and ice lost by melting. The mass balance is a measure of the change in total mass of a glacier during a year. Mass balance is measured in terms of the addition of mass to the glacier, or **accumulation,** and the loss of mass from the glacier, or **ablation.**

The mass balance is positive when a glacier gains more mass during a year than is lost, and negative when more mass is lost than gained. A succession of years in which the mass balance is positive means that the glacier increases in mass, and its front end or **terminus** advances. A series of years in which the mass balance is negative reflects the opposite: the glacier decreases in mass and its terminus retreats.

The glacier system can be divided into two zones: an upper zone, termed the **zone of accumulation**, where there is an area of net gain in mass and a lower zone, called the **zone of ablation**, where there is an area of net loss in mass (Figure 6.8). These two zones are separated at the **equilibrium line**, where net loss of mass equals net gain. When balanced or steady state conditions exist, the **equilibrium line** is at a particular altitude midway between the start and terminus of the glacier. But the equilibrium line is very sensitive to climate; in years of negative balance it is higher and in positive years it is lower.

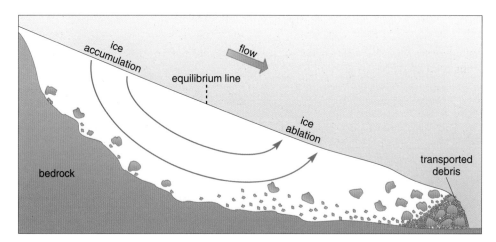

Figure 6.8   Zones of accumulation and ablation on a glacier. The equilibrium line separates the two.

Figure 6.9 shows maps of the South Cascade Glacier in Washington State at the end of 1963 and 1964. The solid line indicates the equilibrium line the glacier would have if balanced (steady-state) conditions were prevalent. The graphs show mass balance against altitude. The dashed lines on the glaciers show the actual equilibrium lines. In 1963, when there was a negative balance indicating a loss of mass, the equilibrium line is higher than the steady state line. In 1964, when there was a positive balance indicating a gain of mass, the equilibrium line is lower than the steady state line.

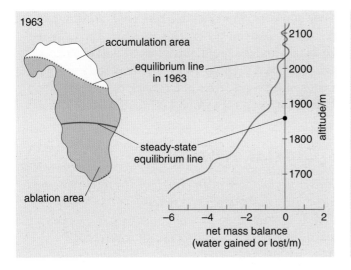
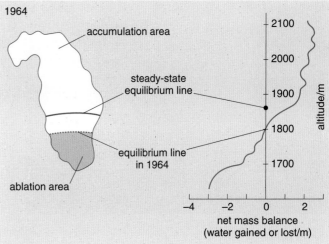

Figure 6.9 The equilibrium lines and mass balance for the South Cascade Glacier in Washington State at the end of 1963 and 1964.

6.4 Non-equilibrium behaviour in glaciers

Occasionally, the flow of a glacier will experience an unusually rapid movement called a surge. Such an event is usually preceded by a period of stagnation in the lowest part of the glacier, and as the surge begins the boundary between active ice in the upper glacier and the stagnant ice below moves rapidly downslope. Surges can involve flows 100 times greater than normal and can result in an advance of the glacier terminus by up to several kilometres. Surging is thought to result from the build up of water at the base of the glacier leading to periods of enhanced basal sliding.

BASAL sliding.
=

○ How could we recognize a surging glacier?

● Surging glaciers are recognized by the contorted folding of bands of rock debris caught up in the ice (Figure 6.10b). This contrasts sharply with the parallel lines seen in non-surging counterparts (Figure 6.10a).

(a)

(b)

Figure 6.10 Non-surging and surging glaciers. (a) The parallel banded moraines of the Barnard Glacier in Alaska indicate normal flow while (b) the contorted moraines of the Tweedsmuir Glacier, also in Alaska, indicate surging flow.

Figure 6.11   A calving glacier.

Figure 6.12   Glacial striations.

lee side ?

A glacier will come to a dramatic halt when its terminus reaches a large body of water. This is due to a process known as calving: the progressive loss of portions of glacier ice into a deep body of water. Many icebergs enter the oceans of the world from the calving of the Greenland and Antarctic glaciers (Figure 6.11).

6.5 Glacial erosion

Glaciers erode by three main processes. At the simplest level glaciers can scoop up and remove soil and weathered rock debris as they flow. The ice at the base of glaciers freezes to the bedrock, usually exploiting joints and fractures. It plucks out attached material as the glacier moves, and carries it away trapped in the ice. Unsurprisingly this process is called plucking, and is at its most intense on the lee side of hillocks and rock mounds. An example of this process can be seen in the asymmetric features known as **roches moutonnées**, which in French means 'fleecy rocks'. We will return to examine this glacial feature in Section 6.5.2. The 'upstream' side of a roche moutonnée slopes gently, and is polished and striated due to abrasion, while the 'downstream' side is steep, irregular and jagged due to glacial plucking.

Once fragments of rock are trapped in the ice they can form an abrasive which grinds away the bedrock during transport. This process is termed **scouring**. Scouring creates a variety of features, the most conspicuous of which are glacial **striations**. These are long parallel lines scratched into the bedrock by rock debris trapped in the base of a glacier (Figure 6.12).

○ How can striations be used to reveal the direction of past ice flow?

● The long axes of the striations will be parallel to the flow of ice.

6.5.1   Erosional landforms of valley glaciers

Valley glaciers create a number of characteristic landforms (Figure 6.13). **Cirques** are bowl-shaped depressions on mountain sides which are produced by erosion at the head of a glacier (Figure 6.14). These landforms probably start to develop beneath a snowfield where frost shattering eats away at the rock and meltwater removes the resulting debris. As the snowfield becomes a glacier, plucking and abrasion enlarge the depression. Once a cirque no longer contains a glacier it may be filled with a small lake or **tarn**. Two adjacent cirques may meet to form jagged, serrated linear ridges called **arêtes** (Figure 6.15). If several cirques meet, a pyramid-shaped peak or **horn** may result, the most celebrated example of which is the Matterhorn in the Swiss Alps (Figure 6.16).

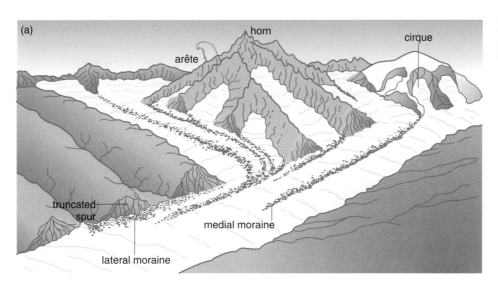

(a)

horn

arête

cirque

truncated spur

medial moraine

lateral moraine

Figure 6.13 The landforms produced by valley glaciers, (a) during and (b) after glaciation.

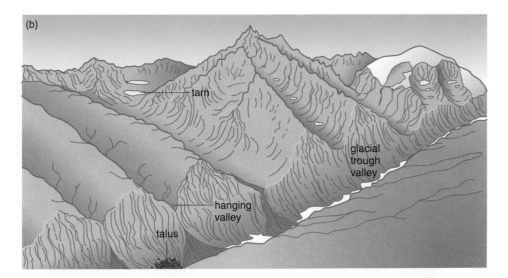

(b)

tarn

glacial trough valley

hanging valley

talus

Figure 6.14 A cirque. Mt Whitney, Sierra Nevada, California, USA.

Figure 6.15 An arête. Striding Edge, Lake District, UK.

Figure 6.16 The Matterhorn, a horn in the Swiss Alps.

Glaciers exploit pre-existing stream valleys, and the modified valleys are themselves distinct landforms. Streams erode along an extremely narrow line in the lowest part of a valley, whereas a glacier is in contact with a much greater proportion of the valley floor and sides. This more widespread erosion converts pre-existing 'V' shaped stream valleys into trough-like or 'U' shaped **glacial trough valleys** with steep sides and a flat floor. Above the height of the surface of the glacier, the valley sides remain relatively undisturbed. Any ridges that projected into the original stream valley sides will be cut back to create **truncated spurs**. Glacial valleys have floors that have been eroded to levels well below the floors of tributary valleys and, once the ice has retreated, these tributaries sit high above the main valley floor and are referred to as **hanging valleys**.

Repeated freezing and thawing of bedrock produces significant amounts of shattered, angular rock fragments. The rock fragments accumulate at the base of steep slopes and are known as **talus**. Much of the debris carried by an alpine glacier comes from valley sides where talus accumulates.

6.5.2 Erosional landforms of ice sheets

Ice sheets cover extensive landscapes that contain both high mountains and areas of low relief. Consequently, the landforms produced by ice sheets are more diverse and widespread than those produced by valley glaciers. Areas glaciated by ice sheets show striations on bedrock surfaces.

○   How could we recognize the areas where past ice sheets have not completely covered the tops of mountains?

●   The upper limit of the glacier is marked by a change from smooth, abraded slopes to frost shattered ridges and peaks.

Large shallow basins are gouged from soft sedimentary rocks, a number of which exist today as lakes. Many of the lakes on the Canadian Shield, including those of the Great Lakes, were created by glacial erosion (Box 6.1).

Near the edges of ice sheets the underlying topography is moulded into smooth, parallel ridges (Figure 6.18). As an ice sheet expands it strips the underlying landscape of soil and debris, and the exposed bedrock is eroded into streamlined shapes. These can take the form of roches moutonnées (Figure 6.18a). Another erosional feature is a **crag and tail**, where glacial deposits have collected downstream of a resistant rock knob. Edinburgh Castle, UK, is sited on a crag and tail, taking advantage of the defensive qualities of the steep downstream cliff face (Figure 6.19). Streamlined hills made of glacial deposits, rather than solid rock, are common and are called **drumlins** (Figures 6.18b and 6.20). If an area is totally composed of smoothed forms it is called a **streamlined landscape**.

hanging valley

Box 6.1   The Great Lakes

The Great Lakes straddle the border between the USA and Canada and make up the largest combined body of fresh water in the world. The five lakes — Superior, Michigan, Huron, Erie and Ontario — cover an area of 246 050 km². Lake Michigan alone covers an area of 57 755 km² and can be seen in the centre of Figure 6.17, with Chicago on its southwestern (bottom left) shore. During the last glacial stage this area was covered by an ice sheet that scoured the bedrock to produce enormous basins. At the end of the last glacial stage, about 12 000 years ago, the ice sheet retreated and the basins filled with meltwater.

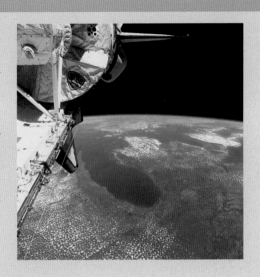

Figure 6.17   The Great Lakes, USA and Canada, the largest combined body of fresh water in the world. Lake Michigan can be seen in the centre of the photograph.

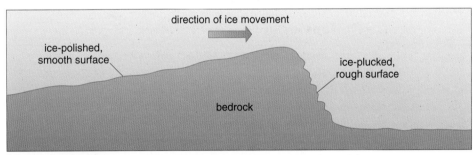

(a) roche moutonnée

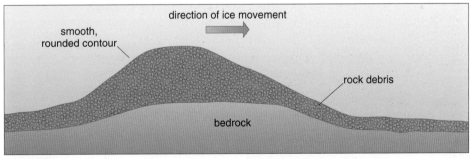

(b) drumlin

Figure 6.18   Two morphologically similar landforms produced by ice sheets: (a) Roches moutonnées are polished outcrops of tough bedrock having one smooth side and one jagged side, created by the flow of an ice sheet; (b) drumlins are long, streamlined hills composed, not of rock, but of rock debris moulded into a mound by a glacial ice sheet.

Figure 6.19 Edinburgh Castle atop a crag and tail.

Figure 6.20 Drumlins, mounds of glacial deposits.

6.5.3 Fjords

Fjords are found along some steep, high-relief coastlines where glaciers flow into the sea (Figure 6.21). The valleys are deep troughs that often extend inland for tens or hundreds of kilometres. Some fjords imply vertical erosion of 300 m or more. Sognefjord in Norway reaches a maximum depth of 1300 m, but near its mouth this reduces to 150 m. This overdeepening of fjords is the result of efficient glacial erosion from thick and fast-flowing ice. Typical examples of fjords can be seen in Norway, Canada, Alaska, Iceland, Greenland, Antarctica, New Zealand, and southernmost Chile.

Figure 6.21 A fjord, Milford Sound, New Zealand.

6.6 Glacial transport

○ How does the transport of load differ in a glacier when compared to a stream?

● In a glacier, rock fragments and particles of various sizes can be carried side by side without segregation by size into suspended load and bedload. As a result of this lack of segregation the deposits left directly by glaciers are neither sorted into sizes nor stratified. In a stream the load is separated into suspended load and bedload, a process which leads to well-stratified deposits.

The load of a glacier is concentrated towards its base and sides, as these are the areas where the glacier is in contact with the bedrock. A certain amount of the load is derived from the collapse of cliff faces adjacent to the glacier and these materials are transported on the surface.

Much of the glacier load is in the form of a fine powder, known as rock flour, which is the product of extensive abrasion. The incorporation of this material into glacial meltwater gives the water a light, cloudy appearance, which has inspired the term 'glacial milk' (Figure 6.22).

Figure 6.22 Glacial meltwater.

6.7 Glacial deposition

Glacial deposition takes place when material is released from the glacier as the ice melts. Consequently glacial deposition takes place below the equilibrium line (see Figures 6.8 and 6.9). Material can be deposited directly from the ice (**glacial deposition**), from ice floating in the sea (**glaciomarine deposition**), or indirectly from glacial ice meltwater (**glaciofluvial deposition**).

6.7.1 Drift

Sediment deposited by glaciers is characteristically heterogeneous, showing great lateral and vertical variations in thickness, composition and texture. Such unsorted, unstratified deposits of unknown origin are given the general term **diamicton**. Once a glacial origin for the sediment has been determined it can be called **drift**. This term originated in the early nineteenth century when it was suggested that the biblical flood of Noah had drifted this type of deposit to its place of deposition. Drift is a general term for glacial deposits and can be subdivided into three types of material with different levels of sorting: till, glacial marine drift and stratified drift.

Till is unsorted drift which has been produced by glacial deposition (i.e. directly from the ice). Scottish farmers used the term 'till' long before questions about the origin of this deposit were raised. Till is a heterogeneous mix of rock fragments. The matrix consists of sand and silt, derived from the abrasion and attrition of bedrock and entrained material, and large abraded and striated rocks and pebbles. Both matrix and larger, elongate rock fragments can be orientated in the direction of flow.

Glacial marine drift is a glaciomarine deposit generated from floating ice bodies. As the floating ice melts the entrained material drops to the sea floor. Glacial marine drift retains none of the orientation sometimes seen in till, but abraded and striated rocks are still present.

Stratified drift is not deposited directly by the glacier but is primarily a glaciofluvial deposit, produced by the glacial meltwater.

○ What features will be present in stratified drift that are not present in till?

● As the name implies, stratified drift is sorted by size and layered, reflecting its glaciofluvial rather than glacial origin.

○ Do you think glaciofluvial processes are the only means of producing stratified drift from glaciers?

● No, sometimes glaciomarine deposits are stratified as material passes down through the water column.

6.7.2 Depositional landforms

In actively flowing glaciers, the glacier's load is released in the lower parts of the glacier where ablation is dominant. It can either be plastered onto the ground or released at the glacier margin where it can accumulate as a **moraine** (Figure 6.23). If the drift is widespread and smoothly plastered onto the land it is known as a **ground moraine**. The drift deposited at the front end, or terminus, of the glacier is called a **terminal moraine** while that deposited at the sides is known as a **lateral moraine**. If two glaciers merge, the adjacent lateral moraines join to form a single **medial moraine** in the middle of the now larger flow.

A glacier or an ice sheet is capable of transporting boulders over great distances. When the ice melts the boulders are left standing, often in regions where the local rocks are much different (Figure 6.24). Blocks of rock transported in this manner are called **erratics**. Large numbers of erratics may fan out from their

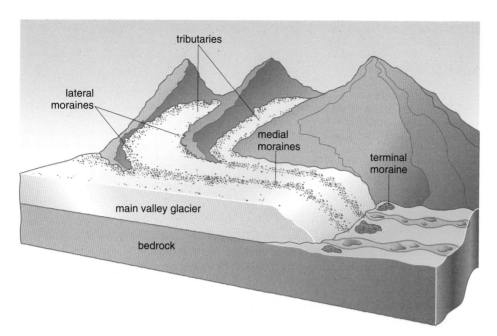

Figure 6.23 Glacial moraines are streams of rock debris transported within the ice. Medial moraines are formed when the lateral moraine of a tributary glacier is incorporated into the main glacier. Terminal moraines are formed by the release of rock debris at the glacier's terminus.

Figure 6.24 Glacial erratic of Silurian Grit perched on a plinth of younger Carboniferous Limestone at Norber Brow, Yorkshire, UK.

source in areas that have been covered by ice sheets and this type of deposit is known as a boulder train.

Glaciofluvial deposits are generated by meltwater from glacial ice.

○ Do you think glaciofluvial deposits will be constrained to within the perimeter of the glacier?

● No. Glaciofluvial deposits are found beyond the glacier terminus as meltwater flows out from the ice and forms streams and lakes.

The stratified drift deposited by glacial streams is termed **outwash** and the large sediment load, steep gradient and variable stream discharge favour the formation of braided streams. If the streams have the space to swing back and forth in front of the glacier they deposit a broad spread of sediments called an outwash plain. Where the streams are confined by a valley then outwash will form a more constrained valley train. Directly in front of the glacier, where water rich in sediment flows off the terminus of the ice, a small mound of sediment, known as a **kame**, can be deposited. Kames are often found on or at the edge of moraines. Glaciers can also contain sinuous glacial streams that flow in ice tunnels at the base of the ice. The beds of these streams remain behind when the ice melts as long narrow ridges known as **eskers**.

○   Hypothetically, how can eskers be quickly distinguished from the contorted medial moraines of a surging glacier?

●   Eskers are glaciofluvial deposits and, therefore, will be composed of stratified drift. Moraines are composed of glacial till which is unstratified.

When glaciers retreat rapidly, blocks of ice can be left behind. Any glacial drift that has piled up around the ice will form a basin when the ice block melts. These hollows are called **kettle holes** and may be filled with water to form **kettle lakes**.

Up to this point we have dealt with landforms that are formed mainly by water, in one form or another. In the next section we will focus our attention on wind. Wind is only an effective agent of change when sediments are dry, as even a thin film of moisture between grains will prevent entrainment by wind because of the high surface tension of water. So next we leave the icy wastes of glaciated landscapes and look at the dry and often searing heat of the desert.

Question 6.1

Examine Figure 6.1 and suggest why this year-round body of ice can be classed as a glacier. What type of glacier is this? Explaining your reasoning, decide whether this glacier is surging or not.

Question 6.2

Look at Figure 6.9 and consider the effect of prolonged global warming on overall mass of ice and the altitude of the equilibrium line for the South Cascade Glacier.

6.8 Summary of Section 6

1   Glaciers are masses of ice that last throughout the year and are capable of flow.

2   Glaciers can be divided into two basic types: valley glaciers, which occur in mountainous regions, and ice sheets and caps, which occur at high latitudes.

3   Glaciers flow due to sliding at their bases and the movement of individual ice crystals.

4   The mass balance of a glacier reveals the balance between the inputs and outputs of the glacier system.

5   A glacier system can be divided into a higher zone of accumulation and lower zone of ablation. These two zones are separated by the equilibrium line, which shifts in response to environmental change.

6   Erosional features, such as cirques, arêtes, horns and glacial trough valleys indicate that glacial action has removed material locally. Depositional features such as moraines, eskers and erratics indicate that material has accumulated locally.

Learning outcomes for Section 6

Now that you have completed your study of Section 6 you should be able to:

6.1   Explain what a glacier is. (*Question 6.1*)

6.2   Recognize different types of glacier. (*Question 6.1*)

6.3   Describe how glaciers move. (*Question 6.1*)

6.4   Outline how glaciers are systems with inputs and outputs of mass. (*Question 6.2*)

6.5   Distinguish between erosional and depositional glacial landforms.

7 Wind

7.1 Aeolian processes

Processes involving wind are termed **aeolian**, after Aeolus, the Greek god of wind (Figure 7.1). The effects of wind are most obvious in the arid and semi-arid regions of the Earth, but are also important along coastlines or anywhere sediment has been recently deposited or is constantly being reworked.

7.1.1 Wind erosion

Wind erosion involves two main processes, **deflation** and abrasion. Deflation involves the removal of unconsolidated material by lifting it into the air or rolling it along the ground (Box 7.1). Deflation occurs whenever the ground surface consists of dry, loose particles and hence affects deserts, beaches, dry river beds and recent glacial deposits. **Blowouts** are deflation basins hollowed out by the removal of particles by the wind. They generally remain small but may enlarge up to kilometres in size. The Qattara depression in the Libyan desert is a blowout that is 300 km across and its floor is 134 m below sea-level.

In some arid areas the removal of fine-grained material leaves behind a cover of residual pebbles which are too large to be removed by the wind, and these form a **desert pavement** (Figure 7.3). These pavements protect finer material beneath and halt further deflation.

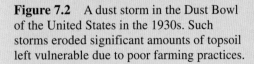

Figure 7.1 Aeolus, the Greek god of wind.

Box 7.1 The Dust Bowl

Perhaps the most celebrated example of wind erosion by deflation was the Dust Bowl of the Great Plains region of the United States (Figure 7.2). During the 1930s, poor farming practices and a period of severe droughts had left large areas of bare soil exposed. Extreme deflation increased average regional erosion rates of a few centimetres per thousand years to a metre or more in a few years. The resulting wind-borne dust clouds were called 'black blizzards' and the period became known as 'the dirty thirties'.

Figure 7.2 A dust storm in the Dust Bowl of the United States in the 1930s. Such storms eroded significant amounts of topsoil left vulnerable due to poor farming practices.

Figure 7.3 A desert pavement.

○ If the closely packed pebble surface of a desert pavement was disturbed, say by a motor vehicle, how would this affect erosion rates?

● The finer material beneath will be exposed and deflation will occur until a new desert pavement is established.

Abrasion occurs when wind propels particles at a cohesive rock and, eventually, wears it down. **Ventifacts** are aerodynamically shaped rocks that have been cut and sometimes polished by the wind (Figure 7.4). **Yardangs** are sculpted landforms streamlined by desert winds (Figure 7.5). In the central Sahara, yardangs may be up to 200 m high and many kilometres long.

Figure 7.4 A ventifact.

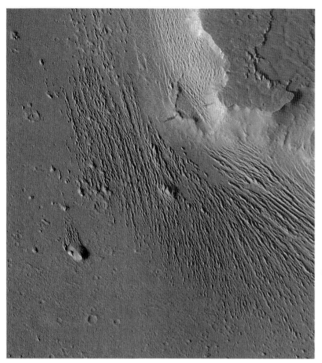

Figure 7.5 Martian yardangs, tens of kilometres long and hundreds of metres high.

7.1.2 Wind transport

Wind exerts similar forces on material on the ground as water does on a stream bed — turbulence and forward motion combine to entrain particles. However, wind is approximately 1000 times less dense than water and is less able to entrain and transport relatively large particles. The amount of material that can be moved by wind increases with wind speed (Figure 7.6), but the ability of wind to erode by deflation and abrasion is reduced by obstacles such as rocks and hills, which increase friction and reduce wind speed.

○ How would strong winds affect the following surfaces: bare sand, grass covered sand?

● The bare sand would be eroded but the grass-covered sand would remain behind.

Vegetation has a dramatic effect on erosion rates and can resist deflation by binding loose particles together and by maintaining a high moisture content. Hence wind erosion is most active in open locations with a sparse or absent vegetation cover.

Once entrained, some fine material is carried by wind in suspension, but the movement of sand-sized particles is usually by saltation. This process occurs in much the same way as in water, but the low density of air allows saltating particles to leap higher. At high wind speeds a dense cloud of saltating particles can hug the ground and sandblast objects in its path. As saltating particles fall to the ground they impact those resting at ground level and force them to shuffle forward parallel to the wind direction. A sand grain striking the ground can push another grain forward by a distance of up to six times its own diameter. This form of aeolian traction is known as **surface creep**.

7.1.3 Wind deposition

Of all the material transported by the wind, the bedload moves most slowly and is deposited quickly, in heaps or small hills, when wind strength drops. Deposits made of bedload form where an obstacle distorts the flow of air. Within a height of a metre or two, the air speed is affected by the slightest irregularity of the surface. When wind meets an obstacle it sweeps over and around it and leaves a pocket of slower-moving air immediately down wind of the obstacle (Figure 7.7a). In these pockets of slower-moving air the eddies generated are weaker than the main wind flow, and the load there is deposited as two separate drifts (Figure 7.7b), before coalescing to form a dune (Figure 7.7c).

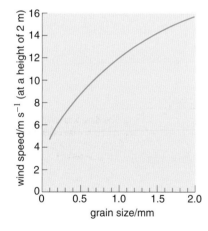

Figure 7.6 The size of grain that can be eroded increases with wind speed.

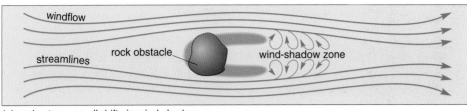

(a) early stage: small drifts in wind shadow

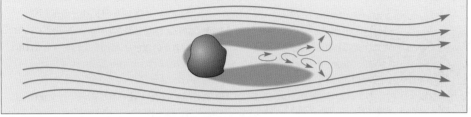

(b) middle stage: large but separated wind-shadow drifts

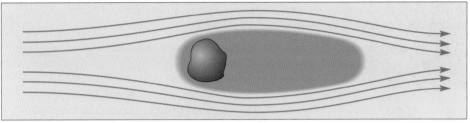

(c) final stage: dune fully developed, wind drifts coalesced

Figure 7.7 Initiation of sand deposition and dune formation in the lee of an obstacle. The object creates a wind shadow with only relatively weak eddies (a), allowing transported particles to settle (b), which eventually form a dune (c).

Dunes are asymmetrical in cross-section and have a steep downwind (**lee**) slope and a gentle upwind (**stoss**) slope (Figure 7.8). Wind moves particles up the stoss slope by saltation and they accumulate on the lee slope, just past the crest of the dune. Eventually this accumulating pile of material becomes unstable and avalanches or 'slips' down the lee slope. This repeated slipping gives rise to the alternative term 'slip face' for the lee slope of dunes. The slip face is always more steeply angled than the stoss slope, and faces downwind. The transfer of sand up the stoss side and down the slip face of a dune causes it to move slowly downwind. The processes that generate and modify dunes operate on all scales (Box 7.2).

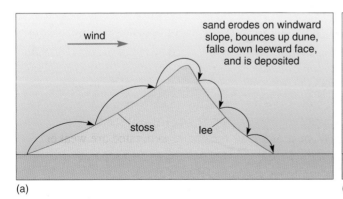

(a)

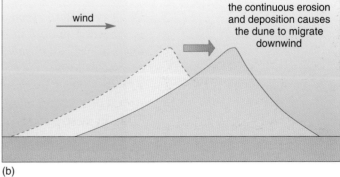

(b)

Figure 7.8 Dune migration.

Box 7.2 Dust storms of the Sahara

Dust storms in three shapes. The whirl. The column. The sheet. In the first the horizon is lost. In the second you are surrounded by "waltzing Ginns." The third, the sheet, is "copper-tinted. Nature seems to be on fire."

Michael Ondaatje, *The English Patient*, 1992.

Dust storms are frequent occurrences in deserts where loosely bound sand grains are easily entrained by the wind. Most grains fall back to the ground within a few hours, but some remain in suspension for days and can be transported thousands of kilometres downwind. Dust from the Sahara Desert regularly crosses the Atlantic, reaching as far as the Caribbean and the Amazon basin. Figure 7.9 shows a major dust storm over northwest Africa, with sand being removed from the Sahara Desert. Note how the path of the suspended load is distorted, creating eddies on the lee side of the mountainous Canary Islands in the centre of the image. This is a large-scale example of the process illustrated in Figure 7.7.

Figure 7.9 A major dust storm over northwest Africa with sand being removed from the Sahara Desert. Note how the path of the suspended load is distorted on the lee side of the mountainous Canary Islands in the centre of the image.

7.2 Aeolian landforms

Accumulations of wind-transported material can be classified according to three fundamental properties: their scale, form and complexity.

7.2.1 Scale

Landforms made of wind-deposited bedload occur at three scales: ripples, dunes and **draas**. Ripples form when wind blows on a sand surface, with the ripple crests being perpendicular to the wind direction. The wavelength of the ripples is determined by the average distance that sand particles jump during saltation. Ripple wavelengths are usually measured in centimetres or tens of centimetres (Figure 7.10). Dunes are accumulations of sand blown by wind into a mound or ridge. They have wavelengths measured in tens or even hundreds of metres and heights measured in metres. **Draas** (Arabic for 'arms') are large dunes with wavelengths measured in kilometres and heights measured in tens or hundreds of metres. An even larger-scale feature can also be added at this point, that of sand seas or **ergs**, which are large tracts of shifting sand. By definition, they are over 30 000 km^2 in area and hundreds of metres thick.

perpendicular — @ right angles

○ What do the presence of ripples, dunes and draas tell us about the aeolian processes which occur in an environment?

● These features indicate that similar aeolian processes are operating over a range of scales.

In the Peruvian desert, studies of dunes that are less than 10 m high and influenced by a single wind direction have revealed the following relationship between scale and movement:

$$A = 41 - 3.1H \tag{7.1}$$

where A is the rate of dune movement in metres per year and H is the height of the dune in metres.

Question 7.1

Using this equation, calculate the rate of dune movement for the following dune heights. Enter your data in Table 7.1.

Table 7.1 Dune heights and rates of shift.

H/m	A/m yr^{-1}
0.5	40.5
1	40
2	39
4	37
8	33
10	31

Figure 7.10 Two scales of aeolian landforms: ripples on a dune.

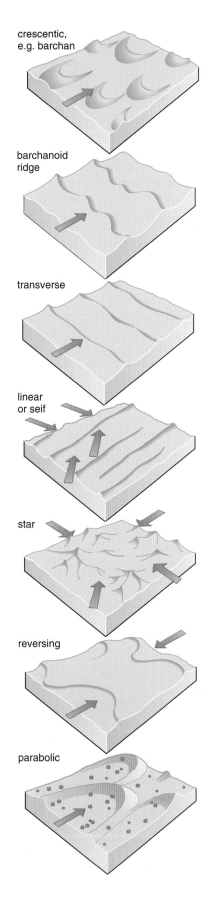

crescentic,
e.g. barchan

barchanoid
ridge

transverse

linear
or seif

star

reversing

parabolic

○ What is the general relationship between dune height and rate of movement in the completed Table 7.1?

● The greater the height the slower the dune moves.

Generally, a taller dune will have a greater volume, and this controls the relationship between dune height and rate of movement. In practice, however, the variation in the data is quite large because factors other than height have an effect.

○ Suggest what these factors could be.

● Different strengths and frequencies of wind occur. Different dune shapes can have the same height but different volumes.

It is the different shapes that dunes exhibit that we turn to next.

7.2.2 Form

Sand bodies can also be classified according to their form (i.e. their shape in plan view and the relative position of their slip faces). They can be crescentic, linear, star, parabolic or reversing (Figure 7.11). This classification system is scale-independent.

Crescentic dunes are crescent-shaped mounds or segments of ridges. Each segment is wider than it is long and is bounded on its concave side by a slip face. Such dunes are found in areas with a single wind direction. There are three main subtypes: **Barchan dunes** are crescents with horns pointing downwind. Barchanoids are rows of crescent shaped dunes. **Transverse dunes** are asymmetric ridges transverse to the wind direction. Crescentic dunes are found in areas of constant wind direction and limited sand supply. They move faster than any other dune type and are generally 1–30 m in height.

Linear dunes are long, straight or slightly sinuous sand ridges. They are found in areas with two wind directions. Slip faces occur alternately on both sides reflecting the dominant wind direction at the time. These forms are also called **seif dunes** after the Arabic word for sword. Linear dunes occur in deserts with scanty sand supply and strong winds. They cover more area in the Earth's deserts than any other dune type and can be 100 m high and 100 km long.

Star dunes are isolated hills of sand with a base that resembles a star in plan. They are found in areas where the wind blows from all directions. They grow upwards reaching more than 100 m in height, and may represent the highest dunes on Earth.

Reversing dunes consist of an asymmetric ridge intermediate in character between a transverse dune and a star dune. They form where strength and duration of winds from nearly opposite directions are balanced.

Parabolic dunes are U-shaped dunes with the open end of the 'U' pointing upwind. Slip faces are found on the outer, convex sides. They are common in coastal deserts and occur where the wind blows from a single direction and vegetation has stabilized the arms of the dunes.

Figure 7.11 Dune forms. Dominant wind directions are indicated by arrows.

○ What do dune forms tell us about prevailing environmental conditions?

● Dune forms indicate wind strength, sand supply and vegetation cover (Figure 7.12). Each form may transform into another and back again as environmental conditions change.

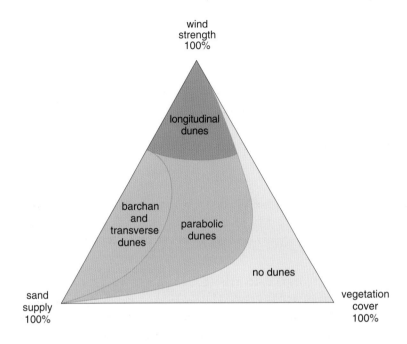

Figure 7.12   The relationship between dune forms and environmental conditions expressed as a ternary diagram. Any point on this ternary diagram represents the relative percentage of three components: sand supply, vegetation cover and wind strength. For instance, at the very top of the triangle we encounter 100% wind strength, 0% sand supply and 0% vegetation cover. Vertically below this point at the base of the triangle we have 0% wind strength, 50% sand supply and 50% vegetation cover.

○ Under what conditions will longitudinal dunes be replaced by barchan dunes?

● An increase in sand supply and a decrease in wind strength.

○ Under what conditions will a vegetated area be replaced by parabolic then barchan dunes?

● A decrease in vegetation cover.

7.2.3 Complexity

Sand bodies can also be classified according to their complexity. They can be simple, compound or complex. Simple dunes are basic forms with a minimum number of slip faces that define the geometric type. They represent a wind regime that has not changed in intensity or direction since formation of the dune. Compound dunes are large dunes on which smaller dunes of similar type and slip face orientation are superimposed. Compound dunes represent a wind regime that has decreased in intensity but not direction. Complex dunes are large dunes that have smaller dunes of different type and slip face orientation superimposed on them.

○ What do complex dunes reveal about wind direction?

● They indicate a wind direction that has changed significantly with respect to both intensity and direction.

7.2.4   Loess

In contrast to the bedload transported by wind, the finer, suspended load travels much faster and further and, when wind speed falls, is laid down as a smooth blanket over the landscape. This type of deposit is called **loess** from the German word for loose, and consists of wind-deposited silt commonly accompanied by some fine sand and clay. Over some wide areas wind-deposited sediment is so thick and uniform that it constitutes a distinct deposit and may dominate the primary landscape (Box 7.3).

Box 7.3   *The world's loess deposits*

The Loess Highland in north-central China, sits at an altitude of 1000 m and extends over an area of 400 000 km² (2.5 times the area of England). It is the world's largest loess plateau and forms part of the drainage basin for the Yellow River. The region is covered by 50–80 m of fine-grained, wind-deposited, yellow silt which smothers the relief of the underlying bedrock. The deposits may have originally formed in areas bordering large continental glaciers where sizeable volumes of meltwater removed the silty rock flour that formed as the ice ground away at the underlying bedrock. When the meltwater dried up, the silt was entrained and transported by the wind in huge dust storms. As the storms abated, the silt was deposited, blanketing the area.

In a similar fashion, the Loess Hills, of Iowa, USA (Figure 7.13) formed between 300 000 and 12 000 years ago when glaciers melted, and rivers transported silt through what is now the Missouri River valley. When the transported silt dried out, it was entrained by strong westerly winds, blown eastward, and laid down as 20–50 m thick accumulations.

Figure 7.13   The Loess Hills, Iowa, USA.

7.3 Summary of Section 7

1   Wind erodes material by deflation and abrasion, and transports it by suspension, saltation and traction (surface creep).

2   Bedload material is deposited in small hills or dunes where there are distortions in the flow of air.

3   These dunes are asymmetrical with a gentle windward slope and a steep leeward slope. The movement of grains up and over the dunes causes the dune to migrate downwind.

4   The same dune forms are repeated on a number of scales.

5   Dunes are present in a number of forms depending on wind strength, direction, sediment supply and vegetation cover.

6   Different scales and forms of dunes can be superimposed to achieve varying degrees of complexity, reflecting variations in wind strength and direction.

7   In contrast to the bedload, the suspended load is laid down as a smooth, blanket-like deposit known as loess.

Learning outcomes for Section 7

Now that you have completed your study of Section 7 you should be able to:

7.1   Explain how wind erodes, transports and deposits material. (*Question 7.1*)

7.2   Outline how dunes are formed. (*Question 7.1*)

7.3   Describe how dunes have different scales, forms and complexities. (*Question 7.1*)

8 Landforms in space and time

8.1 Size and duration of landforms

Landforms are created, they develop, and then they disappear and are replaced by other landforms. Yet the rate at which this process occurs is not the same for all landforms. For example, raindrop impact craters (Figure 8.1) are not as long-lived as mountains (Figure 8.2).

Figure 8.1 Raindrop impact craters.

Figure 8.2 A mountain range, the Stauning Alps, Greenland.

○ Look at Figure 8.3. Can you recognize a relationship between the amount of space a landform occupies and the amount of time it exists?

● It appears that the biggest landforms last for the longest time. For example, our raindrop craters (each a few millimetres wide) last for seconds or minutes, whereas mountain chains can be hundreds of kilometres long and last for tens of millions of years.

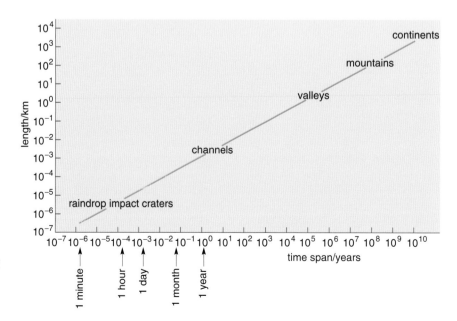

Figure 8.3 The relationship between the size and duration of landforms. The bigger a landform, the longer it takes to erode.

You will recall that we encountered this relationship in Section 7.2.1, where larger dunes appear to move more slowly than smaller dunes. The relationship between size and duration is due to the inputs and outputs of material in the landform system. The larger a landform is, the more material has to be eroded and redeposited to remove it. In addition, this material has to be transported for greater distances. Moving larger amounts of material further distances takes more time.

Learning outcome for Section 8

Now that you have completed your study of Section 8 you should be able to:

8.1 Recognize the relationship between the size and duration of landforms.

Answers to questions

Question 1.1

As you leave the British Isles, you cross the pale blue of the continental shelf. The water then deepens over a small distance. Continuing westwards the depth remains fairly constant (uniform shade of deep blue) before becoming irregular (several shades giving a speckled appearance) and shallower (pale blue) about half way across the North Atlantic. Further westward, the depth to the ocean floor increases irregularly before reaching moderately constant depth again, and then decreasing over a small distance onto the continental shelf of the North American continent.

Question 1.2

(a) The ridge crest is below about 7 mm (equivalent to 3.5 km) of water, and the abyssal plain is about 11 mm (equivalent to 5.5 km) deep.

(b) The height of the ridge can be measured directly or calculated from the answers to part (a): 5.5 km – 3.5 km = about 2 km high.

Question 1.3

Following the Mid-Atlantic Ridge southwards, it splits into two branches. The shorter, westward branch is less distinct than the eastern branch, which is the Southwest Indian Ridge. The latter ridge is followed to the northeast before it splits into the Central Indian Ridge, which connects with the Carlsberg Ridge (which then intersects Arabia), and the Southeast Indian Ridge. The Southeast Indian Ridge can be followed between Australia and Antarctica, before changing its name and becoming the Pacific–Antarctic Ridge. This in turn branches into the East Pacific Rise and the Chile Rise. The Juan de Fuca Ridge, off the western coast of North America, is not connected with the rest of the mid-ocean ridge system.

Question 1.4

Gravitational energy, which affects the water cycle (rain falls downwards because of the Earth's gravitational attraction) and the ocean, causing tides, because of the gravitational pull of the Moon and to a lesser extent the Sun.

Question 1.5

Time = distance travelled/speed, or:

$$t = d/v$$

London is on the Eurasian Plate, and New York on the North American Plate. These plates are separating from each other at a rate of 2.5 cm yr^{-1}, or 2.5×10^{-2} m yr^{-1}. So to travel 1 km, which is 10^3 m:

$$t = 10^3 \, \text{m}/(2.5 \times 10^{-2} \, \text{m yr}^{-1})$$
$$= 4 \times 10^4 \, \text{yr, or } 40\,000 \text{ years.}$$

Question 1.6

The best example of a new ocean is the Red Sea–Gulf of Aden splitting. Another example (although more difficult to see) is the Gulf of California, splitting Baja California from the rest of Mexico.

Question 4.1

If there are six orders of stream in a drainage basin, and there is one sixth-order stream and three fifth-order streams, the following orders will increase geometrically so as to maintain constant ratio. Fourth order = 9, third order = 27, second order = 81 and first order = 243.

Question 4.2

If there are six orders of stream in a drainage basin and the sixth-order stream is 243 km long and the fifth-order stream is 81 km long, the following orders with have lengths that are 0.3 times the previous order, as long as R_L remains at 3.0. Therefore, fourth order = 27 km, third order = 9 km, second order = 3 km, and first order = 1 km.

Question 4.3

Table 4.3 (completed) Characteristics of the Allegheny River drainage basin, Pennsylvania, USA.

Stream order (u)	Number of stream segments (N_u)	Bifurcation ratio (R_b)	Mean length (km) of segments (L_u)	Cumulative mean length (ΣL_u)	Length ratio (R_L)
1	5966	3.9	0.16	0.16	–
2	1529	4.0	0.48	0.64	3.00
3	378	5.6	1.29	1.93	2.69
4	68	5.2	4.02	5.95	3.12
5	13	4.3	11.26	17.21	2.80
6	3	3.0	32.20	49.41	2.86
7	1	–	112.60	162.01	3.50

Question 4.4

During this period three dams were built on the North Platte to store water. These controlled the discharge of the Platte and the variable discharge necessary to maintain braiding was lost. Note also the decrease in stream width as the stream banks are eroded less frequently by floods.

Question 4.5

Potential energy = mgh. Potential energy of water mass in lake $= 5\,000\,000 \text{ kg} \times 9.8 \text{ m s}^{-1} \times 4000 \text{ m}$
$= 1.96 \times 10^{11} \text{ J}$.

Question 4.6

If a stream was dammed both upstream and downstream of a certain location and allowed to dry out, then the dissolved and suspended loads would precipitate and settle, thereby becoming part of the bedload.

Question 4.7

The drainage basin has a dendritic stream pattern indicating an old well-developed drainage surface. The bifurcation ratios for the various stream orders are as follows:

Order	N_u/N_{u+1}	R_b
1	75/17	4
2	17/3	6
3	3/1	3

Question 4.8

A decrease in braiding index and an increase in sinuosity is consistent with a reduction in stream gradient. An imbalance between the load in and out of the stream system indicates that the stream is not yet graded.

Question 5.1

Currently A_d on Assateague Island has been reduced to almost zero due to the trapping effect of the rock jetty. R_d, however, remains the same, and consequently the beach on Assateague Island is receding. When the beach near Ocean City overruns the rock jetty, A_d for Assateague Island will increase and A_d and R_d will be more in balance. At this point, beach recession on Assateague Island should cease.

Question 5.2

Two components can be added to the beach budget equation. A_h, material added by human activity and R_h, material removed by human activity. The full equation for Hallsands would then be:

$$C_f = C_s + A_d + A_w + A_h - R_d - R_w - R_h$$

Question 5.3

1/3 = 0.33, which is greater than 0.25 and therefore the wave is destructive and likely to remove material from a beach.

Question 5.4

The Old Man of Hoy is a sea stack, which is an erosional feature of the coastline. Initially, wave attack on joints and fissures in the sides of a headland would have formed a cave. This cave was eroded until a natural arch developed. Further erosion caused the roof of the arch to become unstable and eventually collapse, leaving an isolated stack.

Question 6.1

The banding on the right-hand side of the ice reveals that the ice mass is flowing and can, therefore, be classed as a glacier. The steep, confining rock walls either side of the ice indicate that this is a valley glacier. The straight moraines indicate that this glacier is not surging and is flowing at a steady rate.

Question 6.2

Prolonged global warming would reduce the input of snow to the glacier and increase the output of meltwater and water vapour. The mass of the glacier would decrease and the equilibrium line would shift to higher altitudes.

Question 7.1

Table 7.1 (completed) Dune heights and rates of shift.

H/m	A/m yr^{-1}
0.5	39.5
1	37.9
2	34.8
4	28.6
8	16.2
10	10

Acknowledgements for Part 1 *Landforms*

Grateful acknowledgement is made to the following sources for permission to reproduce material in this book:

Figures

Cover illustration: Mike Dodd, Open University; *Figure 1.1*: NASA/Goddard Space Flight Centre/SPL; *Figure 1.2a*: N. A. Callow/NHPA; *Figure 1.2b*: Dr Graham J. Potts, University of Liverpool; *Figure 1.2c*: Copyright 2000 Michael H. Reichmann; *Figures 1.2d, 5.16, 6.15*: Kevin Church, Open University; *Figure 1.6*: Northern Ireland Tourist Board; *Figure 1.12*: Woods Hole Oceanographic Institution; *Figure 1.14*: Dave Rothery, Open University; *Figure 1.18*: John S. Shelton; *Figures 2.1, 5.9, 6.20*: GeoScience Features Picture Library; *Figure 2.3*: Image courtesy NASA GSFC, MITI, ERSDAC, JAROS, and US/Japan ASTER Science Team; *Figures 2.5, 4.20, 7.6, 8.3*: Ahnert, F. (1998) *Introduction to Geomorphology*, Arnold, London, Verlag Eugen Ulmer GmbH & Company; *Figures 3.3, 5.9, 5.10, 5.11, 6.14, 6.21, 8.2*: Andy Sutton, Open University; *Figure 3.4*: Stuart Bennett, Open University; *Figures 4.1, 6.22*: Mark Sephton, Open University; *Figures 4.2, 4.17*: Jacques Descloitres, MODIS Land Group; *Figures 4.3, 6.2*: NASA; *Figures 4.4, 4.10*: Sandy Smith, Open University; *Figures 4.5, 4.7, 4.8, 4.9, 5.3, 5.6, 5.14, 6.6, 6.7, 6.9, 7.11, 7.12*: Skinner, B. J. *et al.* (1987) *Physical Geology*, © 1987 John Wiley & Sons, Ltd. This material is used by permission of John Wiley & Sons, Inc.; *Figure 4.6*: SPL; *Figures 4.11, 6.11, 6.12*: Martin Miller, University of Oregon; *Figure 4.12*: NASA JPL TOPSAR; image generation performed at Washington University, St. Louis, USA; *Figure 4.13*: Goudie, A. (1993) *The Nature of the Environment*, Blackwell Publishers Limited; *Figures 4.16, 7.9*: SeaWiFS Project; *Figure 4.18*: Landsat 7 ETM+, copyright ESA 2002, distributed by Eurimage; *Figures 4.19, 4.21, 4.29, 4.32*: © Brian Knapp, Simon Ross and Duncan Macrae (1990) *Challenge of the Natural Environment*, Reprinted by permission of Pearson Education Limited; *Figure 4.23*: Mike Ayres, Open University; *Figure 4.24, 4.25*: Leopold, L. B. and Langbein, W. B. (1996) 'River meanders', *Scientific American,* **214**(6), pp. 60–70, United Press International; *Figure 4.30*: Bob Spicer, Open University; *Figure 5.1*: Doug Houghton; *Figures 5.2, 7.8*: Atkin, B. C. and Johnson, J. I. (1988) *The Earth: Problems and Perspectives*, Blackwell Publishers Limited; *Figures 5.4, 7.2*: NOAA; *Figures 5.5, 6.18, 6.23, 7.7*: Press, F. and Siever, R. I. (1986) *Earth*, 4th edn, © 1986 by W. H. Freeman and Company. Used with permission; *Figures 5.12, 5.15*: London Aerial Photos; *Figure 5.17*: Bird, E. (2000) *Coastal Geomorphology: An Introduction*, John Wiley & Sons Ltd.; *Figure 5.18*: NOAA Coastal Services Centre; *Figure 5.19a*: Courtesy of Mrs C. Blagdon and Plymouth & West Devon Record Office; *Figure 5.19b*: Courtesy of the Coast & Countryside Service; *Figure 6.1*: Bernhard Edmaier/SPL; *Figure 6.3*: USGS/SPL; *Figure 6.4*: Richard Williams/ USGS; *Figure 6.5*: Fuste Raga/SPL; *Figure 6.10a, b*: Austin Post/USGS; *Figure 6.16*: Richard Hodgkins, Royal Holloway University of London; *Figure 6.17*: NASA/SPL; *Figure 6.19*: Malcolm Fife–Edinburgh Photo Library; *Figure 6.24*: Walter Hunt, Open University; *Figure 7.1*: Mary Evans Picture Library; *Figure 7.3*: Geoslides & Geo Arial Photography; *Figure 7.4*: Arne Bomblies; *Figure 7.5*: NASA JPL/MSSS; *Figure 7.10*: Peter Skelton, Open University; *Figure 7.13*: Iowa Tourism Office.

Every effort has been made to trace all the copyright owners, but if any has been inadvertently overlooked, the publishers will be pleased to make the necessary arrangements at the first opportunity.

PART 2
CYCLES

Mark Sephton and Sandy Smith

A cyclic Earth

1

So far in this course we have looked at processes in the four main parts of the Earth (atmosphere, geosphere, hydrosphere and biosphere) mainly independently. In this part of Block 4, we are going to study the Earth as a whole (the '**Earth system**') by considering the connections between these 'spheres', and particularly how chemical elements can move between them. We will start by considering oxygen, the most abundant element in the Earth's crust.

○ List the forms in which oxygen occurs in each of the four spheres.

● Oxygen is a constituent of rocks in the geosphere, for example in silicates, such as granite, or in carbonates such as limestone. In the hydrosphere it is part of the water molecule, also as a gas dissolved in water, and can be part of dissolved compounds. In the atmosphere it occurs as the gases oxygen and ozone, and as a compound with other elements in gases such as carbon dioxide. In the biosphere it is an essential component of living organisms; for example, part of cellulose in woody plants and blood in animals.

Oxygen can also move between the four spheres. For example, in the process of photosynthesis in plants, oxygen derived from water is produced by the biosphere, and released into the atmosphere where it can oxidize rocks during weathering reactions, thereby becoming part of the geosphere. Oxygen-containing minerals in rocks may then be dissolved by water and enter the hydrosphere, and then be utilized by plants, so returning the oxygen to the biosphere.

Thus oxygen, and other elements, can cycle around the Earth. All cycles have some fundamental concepts in common, which give us a way of studying and comparing them. Read Box 1.1 to revise these concepts.

Box 1.1 Cycles, reservoirs, fluxes and residence times

The simplest way to view a cycle is as a box-and-arrow diagram, where the boxes represent places where an element is stored (reservoirs) and the arrows represent pathways of transfer (Figure 1.1a). A cycle is generally drawn for a single chemical element, but sometimes it is drawn for a compound, e.g. water. Figure 1.1b shows these basic elements of a cycle applied to water in a lake. Water enters the lake either from the atmosphere as precipitation or from the land around the lake as stream runoff. It leaves the lake through evaporation to the atmosphere. There is a flux (rate of transfer) and a residence time in each reservoir:

$$\text{residence time} = \frac{\text{amount in reservoir}}{\text{flux}} \qquad (1.1)$$

For example, suppose there is a lake with no surface stream outlet or underground flow, and the only transfer out is by evaporation. We will assume, for simplicity, that the lake is in a steady state, so the volume of water in it does not change with time. For this to be so, the flux of water into the lake must be the same as the flux of water out of the lake. Suppose the lake contains $3 \times 10^6 \, \text{m}^3$ of water, and $3 \times 10^3 \, \text{m}^3$ of water evaporates every day, and the combined amount of water precipitating onto the lake and flowing into the lake is also $3 \times 10^3 \, \text{m}^3 \, \text{d}^{-1}$ (so that the volume of water in the lake remains constant). Then the average residence time (the average time a molecule of water spends in the lake) is $(3 \times 10^6 \, \text{m}^3)/(3 \times 10^3 \, \text{m}^3 \, \text{d}^{-1})$, which is 10^3 days (or 2.7 years).

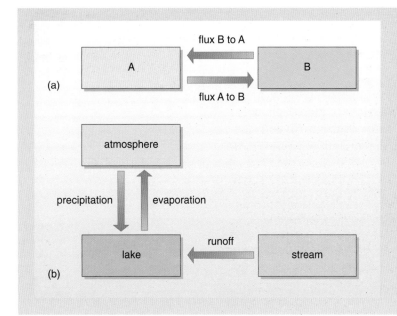

The lake cycle in Figure 1.1b is a small part of the larger hydrological cycle.

The four Earth spheres have different average residence times for the elements in them. In general, the residence time of elements is short in the atmosphere, long in the geosphere, and intermediate in the hydrosphere and the biosphere.

Figure 1.1 (a) A box (reservoir) and arrow (transfer) diagram for a cycle. (b) A box-and-arrow diagram for a lake with no outlet flux to a stream or underground flow.

The main focus of this part of Block 4 is the cycling of some of the elements that are essential to the biosphere, the **biogenic elements**. Their cycles, which are strongly influenced by the biosphere, are called **biogeochemical cycles**. But before we investigate them, we need to study cycling within the geosphere. This is because, ultimately, the geosphere supplies, or has supplied, almost all of the biogenic elements, and additionally cycles these elements, in the rock cycle, which is described in the next section.

1.1 Summary of Section 1

1   Elements can move between atmosphere, geosphere, hydrosphere and biosphere.

2   Biogenic elements are those that are essential to the biosphere. They are cycled within the Earth system between the atmosphere, geosphere, hydrosphere and biosphere. These cycles are the biogeochemical cycles.

Learning outcomes for Section 1

After working through this section you should be able to:

1.1 List the forms in which oxygen can occur in the atmosphere, geosphere, hydrosphere and biosphere, and describe how oxygen can move between these spheres.

1.2 Explain what is meant by the terms 'biogenic element' and 'biogeochemical cycle'.

The rock cycle

2.1 Movement and change in rock

Rock from the continental crust can be eroded, deposited as sediment on the ocean floor, and then it may form new continental rocks during continental collision. This process, and other aspects of continental and oceanic growth that result from plate tectonics, are examples of how rocks are formed and destroyed on the Earth. As you are reading this, rocks are being heated and compressed in mountain belts at convergent plate boundaries to form new metamorphic rocks; other rocks at mid-ocean ridges and subduction zones are melting to form magmas that eventually cool to give new igneous rocks; and the erosion of rocks provides material for the formation of new sediments. For example, each grain of sand or mud in a river estuary was derived from weathering and erosion of rocks further upstream. The liberated particles were transported by the river and eventually deposited. Over many centuries, these sediments may become deeply buried under more sedimentary material, causing the compaction and cementation that produces a sedimentary rock. Thus, the rocks of the mountains can be remade as sedimentary rocks. But what is the origin of the rocks that were eroded to produce the new sediments?

Any sedimentary rock must have been formed by a sequence of weathering, erosion, transport and deposition that is not too dissimilar to that forming new sediments today. Here is the germ of a startling conclusion: the continual action of rock-forming processes means that the rocks of the Earth's crust become transformed and retransformed into new types of rock. The rocks making up the cliffs at the shore, or high mountain crags, are made from materials that were once parts of some other rocks. And, given time, these same cliffs and crags will themselves be transformed, a fact that will be only too familiar if you live in an area subject to the effects of coastal erosion. So we have the indication of a cycle, analogous to the hydrological cycle, in which any rock may become converted into other rock types. This is the **rock cycle**, a complex cycle in which rocks are continually formed and destroyed.

Figure 2.1 illustrates the simplicity of the rock cycle: the three classes of rock are linked by arrows, indicating that any type of rock can be converted into any other type.

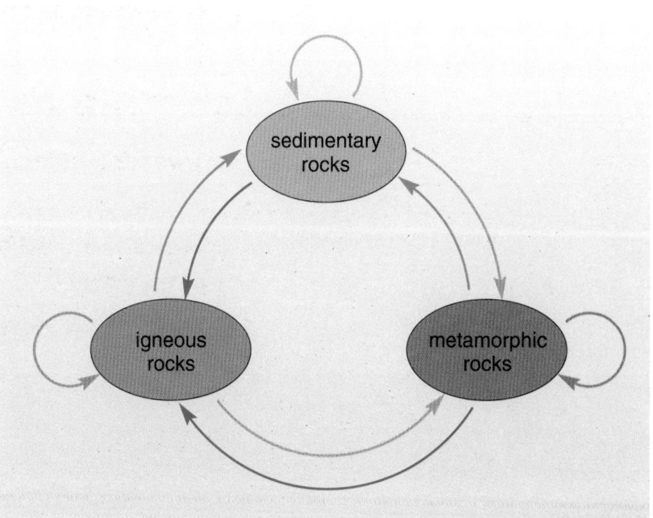

Figure 2.1   A schematic diagram of the rock cycle. The blue arrows represent formation of sedimentary rocks, red arrows formation of igneous rocks, and yellow arrows formation of metamorphic rocks.

○ How many arrows lead to each class of rock?

● Three. One arrow comes from each of the other rock classes, and one is a loop within the class.

Each set of three coloured arrows is associated with one general type of rock-forming process. Thus, the blue arrows in Figure 2.1 represent the sedimentary processes by which sedimentary rocks form from pre-existing rocks of any type. Yellow arrows represent the formation of metamorphic rocks from any other rock, be it sedimentary, igneous or metamorphic, by recrystallization as a result of deep burial and/or heating. Igneous rocks form (red arrows) when magmas cool, and most magmas are produced by the melting of mantle peridotite. However, some magmas form when existing metamorphic, sedimentary or igneous rocks become so hot that they melt.

Figure 2.1 is a purely schematic representation of the important idea that all types of rock can be derived from, or lead to, another type of rock. An alternative way of illustrating the possible ways of moving material around the rock cycle is with a diagram that places the processes into their geological contexts. Since the rock cycle involves processes occurring on the Earth's surface and also within its interior, we use a cross-section through the Earth, as shown in Figure 2.2. In this diagram we have concentrated on the most prominent processes within the rock cycle.

Figure 2.2 The rock cycle. The arrows show the paths and processes taken in transforming one type of rock to another type. Two other cycles interact with the rock cycle — the tectonic cycle and the hydrological cycle.

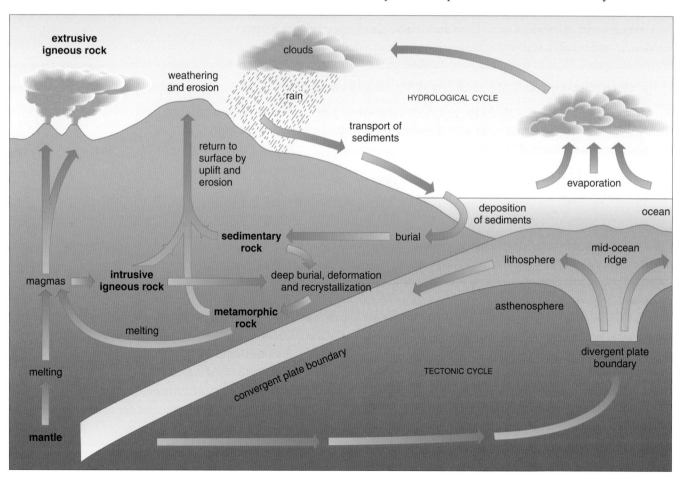

A sedimentary rock may be turned into sediment, redeposited and subsequently turned into a new sedimentary rock. However, the new sedimentary rocks are not just the old sedimentary rock stuck back together again after having been broken apart and transported. Some of the original mineral grains will have been dissolved and some will be transported further than others, becoming deposited alongside grains from other rocks. If you examine some grains of sand from a beach, you'll generally find some broken fragments of sea-shells; these certainly weren't part of the rocks supplying the mineral grains. Likewise, magmas are formed by *partial* melting of pre-existing rocks, so the original rock does not get entirely converted to magma. Of the processes that move material around the rock cycle, only metamorphism involves the conversion of one rock type to another without it gaining or losing any material.

The rock cycle operates because the sedimentary, metamorphic and igneous processes are maintained by the dynamic nature of the Earth. On the grand scale of the Earth, it is plate tectonics that drives many of the rock-cycle processes, with activity being concentrated at plate boundaries rather than distributed evenly over the Earth.

○ Suggest a plate-tectonic setting where metamorphic processes might take place.

● The increases in pressure and temperature needed to cause metamorphism in the crust occur in continental collision zones. Metamorphism also occurs in the crust within subduction zones where rocks get dragged down to great depths and hence experience great pressure.

○ In which plate-tectonic settings do igneous processes take place?

● Melting takes place mainly in the mantle beneath divergent plate boundaries and above the subducting plate at convergent plate boundaries; but it can also take place far from plate boundaries.

Sedimentary rocks form under a great variety of circumstances, such as glacial environments, deserts and the coral reefs on continental shelves. Some great rivers, such as the Nile in Egypt and the Mississippi in the USA, transport sedimentary material many thousands of kilometres across plate interiors, laying down fertile muddy sediments and modifying the coastline by forming deltas. Other great rivers, such as the Ganges, Indus and Brahmaputra (on the Indian subcontinent), rise in the high mountain belts where plates are colliding. In these collision zones, plate convergence thrusts mountains into the sky, but the steep mountain slopes and high rainfall encourage weathering and erosion, with the net result that sites of mountain building are actually prodigious suppliers of sediment, which gets washed away to be deposited elsewhere. The Bay of Bengal contains several million cubic kilometres of sediment that has been removed from the Himalayan Mountains by erosion and transported to the sea.

Plate tectonics thus maintains the rock cycle, not only by producing metamorphic and igneous rocks at plate boundaries, but also through its influence on sedimentary processes. The connection of the rock cycle with the tectonic cycle, which involves the creation and destruction of lithosphere, is shown in Figure 2.2.

The hydrological cycle also drives some of the processes in the rock cycle — the processes involving the formation of sedimentary rocks. Water is involved in the physical and chemical weathering of rocks, the transport of the weathered particles and dissolved material, and the deposition of this material on land or in the ocean. These sediments may then become compacted and cemented into sedimentary rocks (Figure 2.2).

Figure 2.3   A coral reef. These are colonies of tiny coral animals, which build calcium carbonate structures. The animals extend minute filaments from their protective homes to filter plankton from the water.

Life processes also play an important role in the rock cycle. An obvious example is the formation of limestones. For example, chalk (a type of limestone) is formed from sediments composed of the remains of countless microscopic organisms which secreted protective shells made of calcium carbonate ($CaCO_3$). Other limestones are formed from the calcium carbonate shells and skeletons of larger organisms. Similarly, modern coral reefs are built of communities of coral organisms, which also form calcium carbonate structures for protection and defence (Figure 2.3).

Another way in which the organisms in the biosphere affect the rock cycle is through weathering. Rocks are partly broken down by the physical action of wind, rain, ice and extremes of temperature, but this is greatly accelerated by plant roots, microbes and other living organisms in the soil. The action is partly physical — think of tree roots lifting pavement slabs, or saplings wedged in the cracks in a boulder — but the most important process is chemical. A lichen slowly crumbling a stone wall is doing so through chemical weathering, and is forming soil for other plants to establish themselves and continue the process.

The contribution to weathering by organisms results in soil and an increased amount of sedimentary material in the rock cycle. Most of the Earth's soil and a significant amount of sedimentary rock — that derived from carbonate sediments formed by organisms and that derived from sediments due to plant-enhanced weathering of rock — are the products of biological processes. Not only does life require the environment generated by the rock cycle, but some of that very environment is the product of life!

Question 2.1

What form or forms of energy drive the rock cycle?

2.2 A closed or an open system?

There is a fundamental question to consider: is the amount of material in the rock cycle constant, or has it changed during the Earth's history and if so, is it still changing? To investigate this, it is useful to start by considering the rock cycle in terms of a closed or open system. The system concept was introduced in Block 2, Part 1 and developed in Part 1 of the present block, but we need to go a bit further with the concept here, by considering energy (Box 2.1).

Box 2.1   Systems and energy

The system concept is a way to break down any large complex problem into smaller, more easily studied pieces. A system can be defined as any portion of the Universe that can be isolated from the rest of the Universe for the purpose of observing and measuring changes. The system can be whatever the observer defines it to be. That is why a system is only a concept; its limits can be chosen for the convenience of study. It can be large or small, simple or complex. You might study a lake, an ocean, a volcano, a mountain range, a continent, the Open University or even the whole Earth — the Earth system.

The fact that a system has been isolated from its surroundings means that it must have a boundary that sets it apart from its surroundings. The nature of the boundary is one of the most important defining features of a system, leading to the three basic kinds of system — isolated, closed and open — as shown in Figure 2.4. The simplest kind of system to understand is an isolated system; in this case, the boundary is such that it prevents the system from exchanging either matter or energy with its surroundings. The concept of an isolated system is easy to understand but, although it is possible to have boundaries that prevent the passage of matter, in the real world it is

impossible for any boundary to be so perfectly insulating that energy can neither enter nor escape.

The nearest thing to an isolated system in the real world is a closed system; such a system has a boundary that permits the exchange of energy, but not matter, with its surroundings. To a close approximation, the Earth is a closed system. Energy enters and leaves, but except for a few meteorites arriving from space and a tiny amount of gas leaking away from the atmosphere, the Earth has a nearly constant mass. The third kind of system, an open system, is one that can exchange both energy and matter across its boundary. The hydrological cycle of Great Britain, on which the rain is falling, is a simple example of an open system: some of the water runs off via rivers or seeps downward to become groundwater, while some is used by plants or evaporates back into the atmosphere. The atmosphere, geosphere, hydrosphere and biosphere are each an open system, as matter and energy can move between them. These four systems can be subdivided into smaller parts, which may be more manageable systems to study. The rock cycle is a subdivision of the geosphere system.

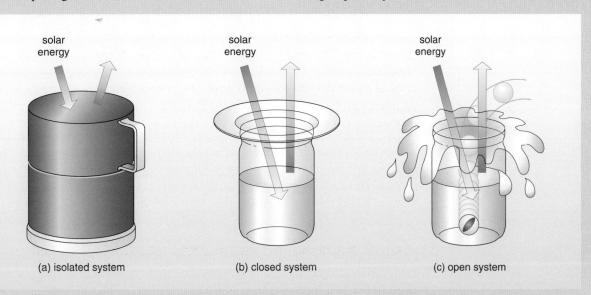

(a) isolated system   (b) closed system   (c) open system

Figure 2.4   (a) An isolated system allows neither energy nor matter to cross its boundaries. Isolated systems do not really exist. (b) A closed system allows energy but not matter to cross its boundaries. Closed systems are rare; but the Earth is a natural example of a closed system, to a close approximation. (c) An open system allows both energy and matter to cross its boundaries. Open systems are common; most of the Earth's subsystems are open systems. The arrows represent energy flows.

○ Why is the rock cycle described as an open system?

● Because the rock cycle has processes that involve the other main systems on the Earth and the exchange of matter between them (for example, the formation of carbonate sediments by life processes). It allows both matter and energy to cross its boundaries.

Now consider a larger system, one that includes not only the rock cycle, but also the hydrosphere, atmosphere and biosphere. This would be a system in which biogeochemical cycles operate. Is this a closed system, in which the amount of each biogenic element is constant, or does it interact with other systems, giving a continual change in the amount of matter within it?

○ What are the two other main systems that this biogeochemical cycle system could interact with?

● Space (outside the Earth's atmosphere) and the interior of the Earth.

We have already noted that the Earth is approximately a closed system, with very little matter exchanging with space. Interaction between the surface system of the Earth and its interior is more complex. The connection between the two is provided by the (plate) **tectonic cycle**, in which lithosphere is created from mantle rocks and also destroyed by re-assimilation into the mantle (Figure 2.2). So the surface and interior systems of the Earth are open systems with matter and energy exchanging between them. A silicon atom, for example, in the surface system may have been in the mantle, and may return to it.

But now for the tricky part. Although there is an exchange of matter between the Earth's surface and the interior, is the rate of transfer of matter from the interior to the surface exactly balanced by the rate of transfer of matter from the surface to the interior, which would result in a constant reservoir of matter in the surface system? Or is there a higher rate of transfer in one direction? This would result in an increase of matter in one system. Or, even more complex, do different chemical elements have different transfer rates to and from the surface system, so there is a gradual build-up of some elements and loss of others?

We need to look at the tectonic cycle in more detail to answer these questions, particularly processes at divergent and convergent plate margins. At divergent plate margins, new basaltic ocean crust is formed by partial melting of the peridotite mantle. This then moves as part of an oceanic plate towards a convergent plate margin. But is this ocean crust in the tectonic cycle isolated from the components of the surface system? The newly formed ocean crust is very hot at divergent plate margins, the mid-ocean ridges. The crust cracks as it cools, allowing seawater to circulate within it. This hot seawater is very effective at weathering the basalt, exchanging ions between the seawater and rock. Sodium is the most abundant cation dissolved in seawater. Sodium ions are exchanged for calcium ions in the basalt, which are released into seawater. So divergent plate margins are sites of exchange of elements between the ocean crust (cycling between lithosphere and the Earth's interior) and the hydrosphere.

Convergent plate margins are also sites of interaction between the surface and interior. Is all the oceanic crust here returned to the mantle, or does some of it join the rock cycle, remaining as part of the continental crust above a subduction zone? Also, is part of the continental crust subducted?

Almost all the basaltic ocean crust is recycled back into the mantle at subduction zones. However, there are two ways by which a small proportion of it is added to the continental crust and becomes part of the rock cycle and surface system. The first way is when relatively small slivers of oceanic lithosphere occasionally escape subduction and form part of the plate above the subduction zone. The second way is when part of the subducting oceanic lithosphere melts, forming magma which rises into the overlying crust. This can solidify at depth, or melt existing crust and continue to rise to erupt at the surface as a volcano.

Question 2.2

Examine Figure 2.5, then comment on whether it provides evidence that volcanoes erupt only magma, or whether they can add matter to the atmosphere or hydrosphere.

Volcanoes can erupt a variety of gases, the most abundant of which is water vapour. A large proportion of this is rainwater trapped in near-surface rocks that is boiled off, but some comes from the magma itself. This can be derived from melting of part of the subducting oceanic lithosphere, but some is new (called 'juvenile') water, which is an addition to the hydrosphere from the Earth's interior. This contribution may appear insignificant initially, but over the Earth's history almost all the water in the hydrosphere came from the interior via volcanoes. The other main gases from volcanoes are sulfur dioxide (SO_2), carbon dioxide, hydrogen sulfide (H_2S), hydrogen and hydrogen chloride (HCl), some of which may come from the continental crust, and some from the interior.

Figure 2.5 The crater lake of the volcano Poas, in Costa Rica.

Another process at convergent plate margins can remove continental crust from the rock cycle to the interior. Erosion of continents produces rock and mineral fragments and dissolved material that may end up as new sedimentary rock on land or on the ocean floor. When this reaches a subduction zone, most of this sediment, having a low density, is scraped off the descending plate, onto the upper continental plate, as part of the rock cycle (Figure 2.2). However, sometimes part of it is carried down with the basaltic ocean crust, and subducted into the mantle. So the tectonic cycle can also destroy continental crust as well as form it.

Question 2.3

Summarize the interactions between the surface system of the Earth and the interior system, by listing (a) transfer processes from the interior to the surface and (b) transfer processes from the surface to the interior.

To return to our original question: is there a balance between the fluxes of matter between the interior and the surface? It turns out that the answer is 'No'; the tectonic cycle acts to produce a *net* transfer of matter from the interior to the biogeochemical surface system of the Earth. This means that over geological time the continental crust is increasing in size (and the oceanic crust decreasing, to maintain the Earth's surface area) and the volumes of the hydrosphere and atmosphere are increasing. In day-to-day terms the increases are minimal, but over the 4600 Ma of the Earth's history, the tectonic cycle (in conjunction with life processes) has profoundly changed the Earth's biogeochemical surface system.

2.3 Rates of change

Earth cycles proceed at widely differing rates, and at rates that vary from one part of a cycle to another. For example, in the hydrological cycle, the residence time for a water molecule in the atmosphere is around 11 days, whereas in the oceans it is about 4000 years. Residence times in the rock cycle are, not surprisingly, much longer than this. But how long is 'much longer', and how are these long residence times estimated? We will use one part of the rock cycle, the weathering of continental rock, to illustrate this.

Rock weathering rates are difficult to study because the processes occur slowly. The rates have to be estimated from what remains in the soil and what is transferred to rivers and streams. Estimates of the dissolved and suspended loads of rivers give a global estimate of weathering. However, before looking at the global scale in more detail, read Box 2.2, to engage with weathering rates on a local scale.

Box 2.2 Weathering at Hubbard Brook

The Hubbard Brook Experimental Forest in New Hampshire, USA (discussed in Block 3, Part 1), is one of a number of long-term ecological research sites, and weathering studies have been made there since 1963. Hubbard Brook is a temperate forest, underlain by an impermeable bedrock, in which it is assumed there is no (or minimal) groundwater flow from the area.

Figure 2.6 is a simplified box-and-arrow diagram for an element in this catchment, which can be used to estimate the rate of rock weathering. As the rock weathers, an element (we will use calcium as an example) is released from the rock and either remains as part of the soil, or is removed from the catchment in runoff (making the assumption that the vegetation subcycle is in a steady state, and does not change the overall calcium concentration in the soil). Calcium is also added to the catchment by precipitation. In a steady state

input = output

so that

Ca supplied by rock weathering + Ca in precipitation = Ca in runoff

Rearranging the above equation:

Ca supplied by rock weathering = Ca in runoff – Ca in precipitation

We can get from this equation to the amount (and rate) of rock weathering from the calcium in the rock and the calcium in the soil, using the equation:

Ca supplied by rock weathering = rock weathering rate × (Ca in rock – Ca in residual material in soil)

Combining the last two equations:

rock weathering rate × (Ca in rock – Ca in residual material in soil) = Ca in runoff – Ca in precipitation

Rearranging the above equation:

$$\text{rock weathering rate} = \frac{\text{Ca in runoff} - \text{Ca in precipitation}}{\text{Ca in rock} - \text{Ca in residual material in soil}} \quad (2.1)$$

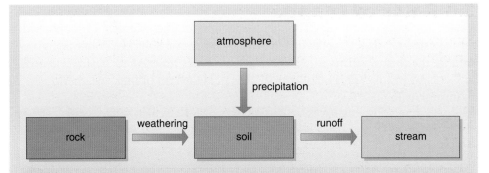

Figure 2.6 A simplified box-and-arrow diagram for an element in the Hubbard Brook catchment. The assumption is made that there is no groundwater inflow or outflow from the catchment and no gaseous exchange (e.g. via respiration). This subcycle links to other subcycles for the element.

Table 2.1 gives rock weathering data for four elements in Hubbard Brook.

Table 2.1 Rock weathering data for Hubbard Brook.

Element	Annual net loss (runoff loss − precipitation input)/ $kg\,ha^{-1}\,yr^{-1}$	Concentration in rock/ $kg\,kg^{-1}$ of rock	Concentration in soil/ $kg\,kg^{-1}$ of soil	Calculated rock weathering rate/ $kg\,ha^{-1}\,yr^{-1}$
Ca	8.0	0.014	0.004	
Na	4.6	0.016	0.010	
K	0.1	0.029	0.024	
Mg	1.8	0.011	0.001	

Using the data in Table 2.1 and Equation 2.1 for calcium:

$$\text{Rock weathering rate} = \frac{8.0\ kg\,ha^{-1}\,yr^{-1}}{(0.014 - 0.004)\ kg\,kg^{-1}}$$

$$= \frac{8.0\ kg\,ha^{-1}\,yr^{-1}}{0.01\ kg\,kg^{-1}}$$

$$= 800\ kg\,ha^{-1}\,yr^{-1}$$

Question 2.4

Calculate the rock weathering rates using the data for the other three elements in Table 2.1, and put the answers in the right-hand column of the table.

The calculations show different rates of rock weathering using the four different rock-forming elements: the observed losses of calcium and sodium in stream water imply higher rates of rock weathering than those calculated using the potassium and magnesium data. This may be because the latter elements are accumulating in clay minerals in the soil. In addition, trees may take up and store essential elements in long-lived tissues (e.g. wood growth), temporarily reducing the loss of some elements in stream water.

The study at Hubbard Brook shows that, even on a small scale, estimates of rock weathering rates can be very variable, depending on the chemical element used for the estimate. Rates can also vary with the type of catchment. Table 2.2 gives data for the flux of *chemical* weathering from other forested ecosystems as well as Hubbard Brook. (This is, of course, less than the rate of *total* weathering estimated in Table 2.1.)

Table 2.2 Net flux (export minus atmospheric deposition) of major ions, soluble silica, and suspended solids from various watersheds of forested ecosystems.

Watershed characteristics	Caura River, Venezuela	Gambia River, West Africa	Catoctin Mountains, Maryland, USA	Hubbard Brook, New Hampshire, USA
latitude	15° S	13° S	39° N	44° N
size/km^2	47 500	42 000	5.5	2
precipitation/cm yr^{-1}	450	94	112	130
vegetation	tropical forest	savannah forest	temperate forest	temperate forest
flux/kg ha^{-1} yr^{-1}	372.7	47.6	220.9	80.4

Fluxes in Table 2.2 vary from 47.6 kg ha^{-1} yr^{-1} to 372.7 kg ha^{-1} yr^{-1} in the four forested ecosystems.

○ Is there a connection between chemical weathering and precipitation?

● At first sight, yes: the forest with the highest precipitation (the Caura River) has the highest flux and that with the lowest precipitation (the Gambia River) has the lowest flux. However, the relationship does not seem to work for the other two forests: the Catoctin Mountains have nearly three times the flux of Hubbard Brook, but slightly less precipitation. The Catoctin Mountains have also nearly five times the flux of the Gambia River, although the precipitation is similar.

More detailed studies indicate that there is a connection between chemical weathering and *runoff*: the greater the streamflow from a catchment, the more dissolved ions are transported. But is runoff the only control for chemical weathering? Chemical weathering also depends on other factors, mainly temperature (increasing with increasing temperature) and the type of rock and pH of the precipitation.

○ Does Table 2.2 indicate this?

● Somewhat — the hot, tropical forest (Caura River) has the highest flux and of the two USA forests, the lower-latitude one has the higher flux.

Data such as those in Table 2.2 can be combined with information from other areas to produce a global figure for chemical weathering. It is estimated that rivers transport around 4×10^{12} kg of dissolved substances to the oceans each year, an average of about 270 kg ha^{-1} yr^{-1} for the land surface.

In addition to chemical weathering, a large amount of material derived from *physical* weathering is eroded from land and carried in rivers as the particulate or suspended load. The global transport of sediment in rivers has been estimated at $(13.5 \text{ to } 16.2) \times 10^{12} \, \text{kg yr}^{-1}$. The total denudation of land is dominated by the products of physical weathering, which exceeds chemical weathering by three to four times worldwide (Table 2.3). The mean rate of total continental denudation is about $1000 \, \text{kg ha}^{-1} \, \text{yr}^{-1}$, with approximately 75% carried in the suspended sediments in rivers.

Table 2.3 Chemical and physical weathering of the continents.

Continent	Chemical weathering		Physical weathering		Ratio physical/ chemical weathering
	Total/ $10^{11} \, \text{kg yr}^{-1}$	Per unit area/ $\text{kg ha}^{-1} \, \text{yr}^{-1}$	Total/ $10^{11} \, \text{kg yr}^{-1}$	Per unit area/ $\text{kg ha}^{-1} \, \text{yr}^{-1}$	
North America	7.0	330	14.6	840	2.1
South America	5.5	280	17.9	1000	3.3
Asia (includes Pacific islands)	14.9	320	94.3	3040	6.3
Africa	7.1	240	5.3	350	0.7
Europe	4.6	420	2.3	500	0.5
Australia	0.2	20	0.6	280	3.0
All continents	39.3	267 (mean)	135.0	918 (mean)	3.4 (mean)

The regional variation in sediment flux from physical weathering and the sediment flux from major river drainage basins are shown in Figure 2.7. The importance of physical weathering increases with elevation; differences in mean elevation among the continents explain much of the variation in physical weathering in Table 2.3. The highest measured sediment yields are from high-precipitation, humid regions and from basins that drain steep, high-relief mountains such as the Himalayas, the Andes and the Alps. The continent discharging the most sediment to the ocean is Asia; it is also the continent on which the greatest average stream sediment loads have been measured. Asian rivers contribute nearly half the total global sediment input to the oceans (Figure 2.7). Second to Asia is the combined area of the large western Pacific Islands of Indonesia, Japan, New Guinea, New Zealand, the Philippines and Taiwan. Mainland Asia and the Pacific islands together contribute about 70% of the global sediment input (i.e. 94.3 of a total for all continents of 134 units — Table 2.3).

The rivers that contribute the most dissolved material are: the Yangtze River, which drains the high Tibetan plateau of China; the Amazon River, which drains the northern half of the Andes in South America; and the Ganges–Brahmaputra river system, which drains the Himalayas in India. Collectively, these three rivers deliver about 20% of the fluvial water and dissolved matter entering the oceans. If we add all the other rivers draining these three highland regions, we find that chemical weathering and erosion in Tibet, the Andes and the Himalayas must provide a substantial part of the total dissolved load reaching the world's oceans.

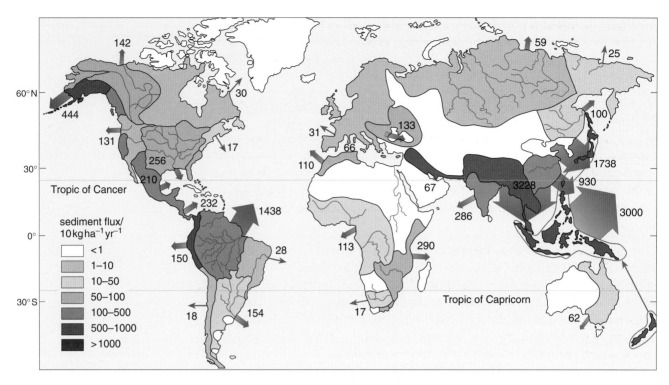

Figure 2.7 Sediment flux from continental physical weathering per unit area, in tens of kg ha^{-1} yr^{-1} (see key). The arrows show the total sediment flux (10^9 kg yr^{-1}) from major river drainage basins. The width of the arrows is proportional to the river sediment flux.

In other words, a direct relationship apparently exists between the occurrence of high-altitude landmasses and the global rate of chemical, as well as physical, weathering.

High rates of weathering and high mountains are related for several reasons. First, high mountains are areas of rapid uplift. They occur where plates of lithosphere converge and cause mountain systems to form. Rapid uplift goes hand-in-hand with rapid physical breakdown and erosion of rock. The disintegration exposes large quantities of rock and mineral debris to chemical weathering. High mountains force moisture-bearing winds upwards and generally receive large amounts of precipitation. This results in high rates of stream runoff and high erosion rates. The effect is especially pronounced in southern Asia where the intense monsoon rainfall on the southern flank of the Himalayas leads to unstable slopes, intense erosion, and a high discharge of dissolved matter and suspended sediment to the Indian Ocean. In South America, more than three-quarters of the dissolved substances carried by the Amazon River to the sea come from the Andean highlands.

Low sediment yields characterize deserts and the polar and subpolar sectors of the northern continents, mainly because of low runoff (Figure 2.7). Rates are higher on steep slopes, and much higher in areas underlain by easily eroded sediments or sedimentary rocks, than in areas where crystalline rocks crop out.

Structural factors also play a role, for rocks that are more highly jointed or fractured are more susceptible to erosion than massive ones. Denudation is surprisingly high in some dry climate regions, an important reason being that the surface often lacks a protective cover of vegetation.

The dominant erosional process can also strongly influence sediment yield. Measurements have shown that sediment yields generally increase with increasing glacier cover in a drainage basin, as glaciers can easily erode and transport large amounts of sediment. Values are unusually high in places like south-coastal Alaska, the most extensively glaciated temperate mountain region in the world. In areas favourable for the expansion of temperate valley glaciers, both chemical and physical weathering rates tend to be substantially higher than the global average.

One important factor that influences denudation rates is human activity, especially the clearing of forests, development of cultivated land, damming of streams and during construction of cities. Each of these activities has increased erosion rates and sediment yields in the drainage basins where they have occurred. On the other hand, once an area has been urbanized, sediment yield tends to be low because the land is almost completely covered by buildings and roads, which protect the underlying rocks from erosion.

In many drainage basins, the measured and estimated sediment yields reflect conditions that are probably quite different from those of only a few decades ago, because much of the sediment that formerly reached the sea is now being trapped in reservoirs behind large dams. For example, the high Aswan Dam on the River Nile, in Egypt, now intercepts most of the sediment that formerly was carried by the Nile to the Mediterranean Sea.

We hope that this discussion of rock weathering rates has given you an indication of how globally variable, and how imprecise, estimates of rock weathering are. Similarly, other parts of the rock cycle are also difficult to quantify with much precision. However, there are some useful values to keep in mind, even if they are rough. The ocean crust has a maximum age of 180 Ma; all older crust (except some small slivers on land) has been recycled into the mantle. Its average age is around 60 Ma. Continental crust can be much older, up to 4000 Ma, with an average of around 650 Ma. This greater age reflects the situation that very little of the continental crust is recycled back into the mantle, so its residence time is very long. Compare this with the 11-day residence time for water in the atmosphere!

Question 2.5

In this question you will draw together information in Figure 2.2 and your knowledge of rocks from earlier in the course to summarize several aspects of the rock cycle.

(a) Which processes in the rock cycle involve the Earth's atmosphere? (b) How might an atom that was originally in the mantle end up in a sedimentary rock? Outline the various ways for the atom to make this journey.

2.4 Summary of Section 2

1   The rock cycle encompasses the formation and destruction of rocks. Rocks are continually being formed and destroyed by geological processes. These include weathering, erosion and deposition, magma generation and metamorphism. All these processes are linked together within the rock cycle. The rock and tectonic cycles supply biogenic elements from the geosphere to the other spheres. The rock cycle interacts with the tectonic cycle and hydrological cycle, and is driven by these two cycles. Life processes can also influence rock cycle processes.

2   Elements are cycled in the Earth system because it is effectively a closed system; energy can cross its boundaries but matter does not.

3   The rock cycle is an open system. New material is added to and removed from the cycle at divergent and convergent plate margins. On a long time-scale, there is a net transfer of material from the mantle to the rock cycle, atmosphere, hydrosphere and biosphere by the tectonic cycle.

4   Residence times in the rock cycle are long in comparison with other cycles.

Learning outcomes for Section 2

After working through this section you should be able to:

2.1 Describe the formation and destruction of rocks in the rock cycle. (*Questions 2.2, 2.3 and 2.5*)

2.2 Explain what drives the rock cycle. (*Question 2.1*)

2.3 Apply systems concepts of matter and energy flow across system boundaries to various types of systems on the Earth. (*Questions 2.2, 2.3 and 2.5*)

2.4 Distinguish open and closed systems. (*Question 2.2*)

2.5 Explain why the Earth is effectively a closed system, and why the rock cycle is an open system. (*Question 2.2*)

2.6 Explain how the tectonic cycle produces a net transfer of material from the mantle to the rock cycle, atmosphere, hydrosphere and biosphere. (*Questions 2.2, 2.3 and 2.5*)

2.7 Order the four spheres by increasing average residence time of elements.

Biogeochemical cycles

3

3.1 Nature recycles

All things begin in order, so they shall end, and so they shall begin again.

The Garden of Cyrus, Sir Thomas Browne (1658)

While the Earth has a continuous supply of energy from the Sun, the Earth's store of materials (excluding small amounts of extraterrestrial material) is fixed and finite. For materials, the Earth is a closed system.

○ What is the main implication for life on Earth of an unvarying amount of the biologically important elements?

● If life is to continue, Nature must recycle.

So, for as long as life has existed on the Earth, the biologically important elements have been cycled, because without this continued use and re-use, life would have exhausted these elements long ago. During cycling, elements are continually transformed from one chemical compound to another as they pass through both the biosphere and geosphere and, for this reason, the process is termed biogeochemical cycling (Figure 3.1).

In this section, we will examine the biogeochemical cycles of four important elements: carbon, nitrogen, sulfur and phosphorus. These elements are important for various reasons. Carbon is the main component of living tissue; all known life is based on carbon. Certain carbon compounds are important greenhouse gases, which regulate the Earth's temperature. Nitrogen is an essential element for life, notably because it forms an integral part of amino acids, the basic building blocks of proteins, and is present in nucleic acids, which are also found in all living organisms. Sulfur is generally present in very small amounts in living organisms, but is an essential nutrient and is found in certain amino acids, vitamins and hormones. Phosphorus is one of the nutrients needed for the healthy growth of organisms in the biosphere. For example, plants cannot grow without phosphorus and animals cannot produce their skeletons without this element. Phosphorus is also an essential constituent of the energy-transferring molecules of living cells and is required for nucleic acid synthesis.

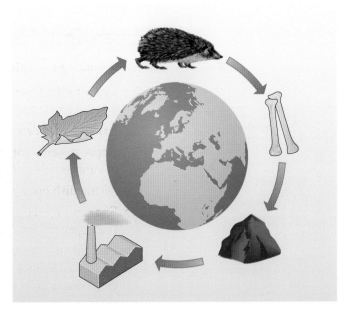

Figure 3.1 On Earth, the biologically important elements are recycled.

The importance of carbon, nitrogen, sulfur and phosphorus to life can be observed by examining Table 3.1, which lists the most abundant elements that go to make up a human being and a green plant, the crop plant alfalfa.

Table 3.1 Chemical compositions of a dried human and dried alfalfa (green plant). Values are percentages by weight.

Element	Dried human	Dried alfalfa
carbon	48.4	45.4
oxygen	23.7	41.0
nitrogen	13	3.3
hydrogen	6.6	5.5
calcium	3.5	2.3
phosphorus	1.6	0.28
sulfur	1.6	0.44
sodium	0.6	0.16
potassium	0.5	0.91

○ Ignoring calcium, which elements are more abundant than sulfur and phosphorus in humans and green plants but have not yet been mentioned?

● Oxygen and hydrogen.

We will not examine the cycling of oxygen and hydrogen in isolation, however, because these two elements are intimately and inextricably linked with the other cycles. Expressed another way, we can say that the transformations within each biogeochemical cycle are essentially oxidation (oxygen addition or hydrogen removal) and reduction (hydrogen addition or oxygen removal) reactions.

So what is it that turns the cycles? Directly or indirectly, it is photosynthesis that provides the energy for all forms of life on the Earth:

$$\text{light energy} + 6CO_2(g) + 6H_2O(l) = C_6H_{12}O_6(s) + 6O_2(g) \qquad (3.1)$$

Photosynthetic organisms capture sunlight, transform it into organic compounds (represented here as the carbohydrate glucose, $C_6H_{12}O_6$), and these organic compounds fuel the biosphere. This stored energy is released via respiration:

$$6O_2(g) + C_6H_{12}O_6(s) = 6CO_2(g) + 6H_2O(g) + \text{energy} \qquad (3.2)$$

Figure 3.2 shows how the photosynthesis and respiration 'couplet' allows energy to be first captured, and then released. As photosynthesis involves the capture of carbon (usually referred to as the 'fixing' of carbon) from the atmosphere or ocean, it makes sense to begin our examination of the biogeochemical cycles with the carbon cycle.

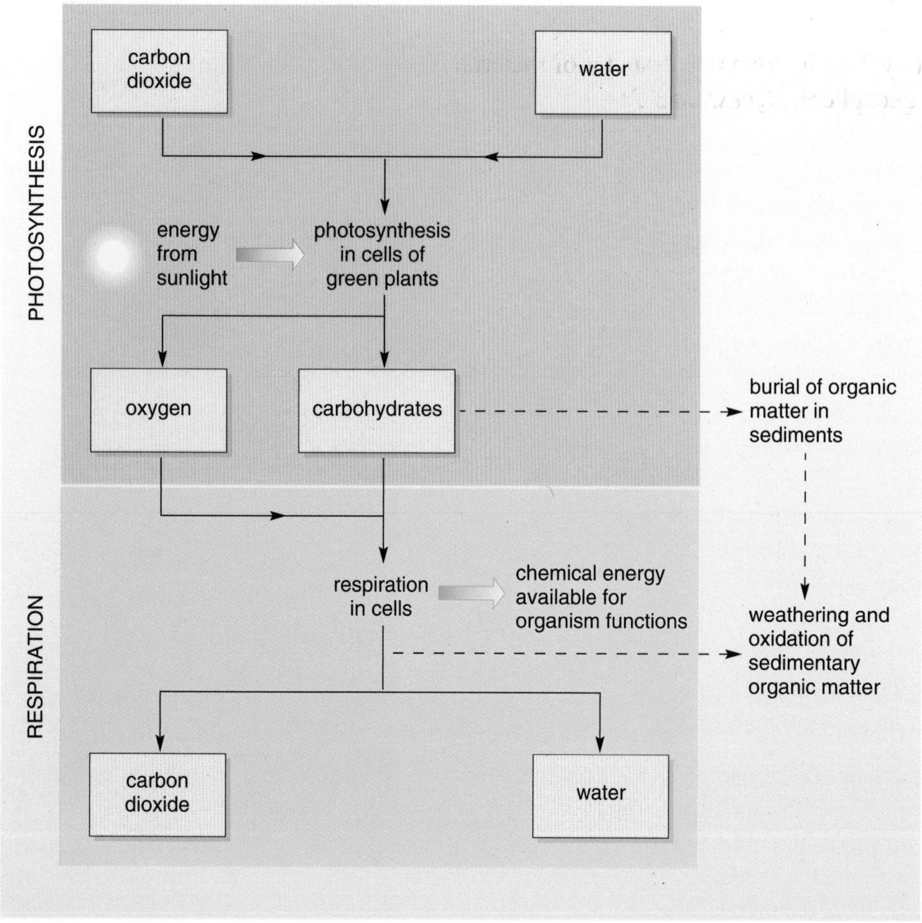

Figure 3.2 The process of photosynthesis captures sunlight energy, which fuels the biosphere: the energy stored in carbohydrates (and other biological molecules) is made available for cell functions by respiration.

3.2 Summary of Section 3

1   The Earth is a closed system for materials. Energy from the Sun arrives continually, but the Earth's store of the chemical elements is finite.

2   For life on Earth to flourish, the elements of which living things are composed must be recycled.

3   Both the biosphere and geosphere are involved in the cycling of elements.

4   Photosynthesis provides the fuel for the biogeochemical cycles.

Question 3.1

What would happen to life on Earth if the biogenic elements could no longer be recycled?

Question 3.2

What does the term 'biogeochemical' tell you about the various reservoirs of the Earth's biogenic elements?

Learning outcomes for Section 3

After working through this section you should be able to:

3.1 Understand that the recycling of elements is essential for life on Earth. (*Question 3.1*)

3.2 Appreciate that biogeochemical cycling involves the transfer of material through both the biosphere and geosphere. (*Question 3.2*)

4

The carbon cycle

The global carbon cycle is central to the workings of the biosphere. Figure 4.1 is a simple representation of the global carbon cycle. Reservoirs of carbon are represented by bold numbers, while fluxes are indicated by arrows and plain-text values. Later you will be able to compare and contrast this simple representation with similar diagrams of other element cycles, but for now we will delve deeper into the inner workings of the carbon cycle to familiarize ourselves with how elements are recycled on the Earth. The carbon cycle involves a hierarchy of subcycles that operate on different time-scales, stretching from years to millions of years. We will begin close to home, studying the short-term terrestrial carbon cycle. Then we will add more and more components, through the intermediate marine carbon cycle and long-term geological carbon cycle, until we have constructed the complete global carbon cycle.

Figure 4.1 The present-day global carbon cycle. The sizes of all reservoirs (bold values) are expressed in units of 10^{12} kg C and annual fluxes in units of 10^{12} kg C yr^{-1}. DOC is dissolved organic carbon; DIC is dissolved inorganic carbon.

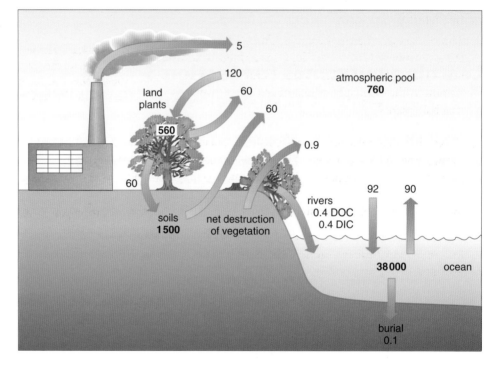

4.1 Short time-scales: the terrestrial carbon cycle

To introduce you to the carbon cycle we will take a journey through one carbon subcycle, that of the terrestrial carbon cycle (Figure 4.2).

Our journey begins with a carbon atom present within a gaseous CO_2 molecule in the atmosphere. This molecule passes through the stoma of a leaf and is stripped of an oxygen atom before hydrogen, other carbon atoms and perhaps nitrogen are attached to it to form one of a variety of organic compounds. Our carbon atom is now part of a plant leaf. Some adjacent leaves are consumed and digested by animals and their carbon atoms are quickly released back to the atmosphere as CO_2 during animal respiration. But our host leaf persists until the autumn before falling to the ground to be subsequently buried under a thick mat of decomposing vegetation. The carbon atom is now part of the soil and it will remain so for about 25 years. During this time the organic matter that contains our carbon atom will be decomposed by bacteria and fungi, which will transform it once again back to gaseous CO_2.

We can now consider the sizes and fluxes of the reservoirs in the terrestrial carbon cycle. You may have noticed that there is no box for terrestrial animal biomass in Figure 4.2. This is because animals are an insignificant carbon reservoir when compared with plant biomass (in fact only about 0.01% of it).

○ What are the relative sizes of the main reservoirs of the terrestrial carbon cycle?

● The reservoirs of plant biomass (560×10^{12} kg C) and the atmosphere (760×10^{12} kg C) are roughly similar but soils (1500×10^{12} kg C) store almost twice as much carbon as the atmosphere and nearly three times as much as plants.

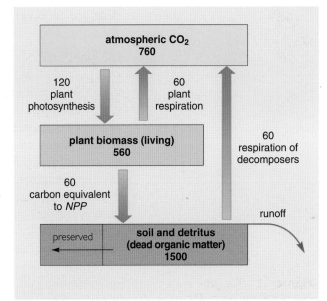

Figure 4.2   The terrestrial carbon cycle. The bold numbers are the sizes of the reservoirs (in 10^{12} kg C) and the numbers beside the arrows are the sizes of the annual fluxes (in 10^{12} kg C yr^{-1}).

The fluxes balance between the reservoirs. Plants convert about 120×10^{12} kg C from atmospheric CO_2 per year. This is the annual terrestrial gross primary production (GPP). About half of this is returned to the atmosphere as respired CO_2.

○ What is the net primary production (NPP), i.e. the net fixation of carbon per year?

● As you learned in Block 3, Part 2, $NPP = GPP - R$, where R is plant annual loss of energy in respiration. Thus $NPP = (120 \times 10^{12}$ kg C yr$^{-1}) - (60 \times 10^{12}$ kg C yr$^{-1}) = 60 \times 10^{12}$ kg yr^{-1}.

Question 4.1

$1500 / 60 - 60 \cdot 0.9 \quad \sim 0.9$

Recalling that residence time = amount in reservoir/(flux to or from the reservoir), calculate the residence time of carbon in soil.

○ Examine Figure 4.2 closely. Is the terrestrial carbon cycle a completely closed system?

● No. Some carbon does 'escape' through preservation and runoff.

On average, the life cycle of a carbon atom in the terrestrial carbon cycle may be repeated over 500 times before the subcycle is broken in one of two ways. Firstly, a small amount of material may never be fully decomposed back to CO_2 and may be preserved as fossil organic matter. Whether organic matter is preserved depends on a number of factors. Some types of organic matter have structural or protective roles for plants and so are highly resistant to decay. One example of a decay-resistant plant material is woody tissue. Anoxic conditions are also strong promoters of preservation. Peat bogs and swamps are oxygen-poor, allowing plant debris to build up and ultimately these accumulations may become fossilized in the form of coal. Secondly, a 'leak' in the terrestrial carbon cycle occurs when, before degradation of the organic matter is complete, carbon is released from the soil by erosion and is transported away by runoff. Removal rates are usually low, but may be higher in certain areas, through soil erosion, exceptionally high rainfall and floods, or human activities such as farming, mining or forestry.

We will assume that our carbon atom has been released from the soil by erosion and the partially decayed organic material of which it is a component has been entrained by running water. The organic carbon transported by water may be either particulate organic carbon (fragments of soil or organic debris) or dissolved organic carbon. But our carbon atom may be joined by inorganic carbon released by the weathering of rocks. We will consider the important effects of rock weathering on the carbon cycle later when we explore the long-term geological carbon cycle. But here we will digress from following the cycle of our carbon atom to remind ourselves of the nature of its inorganic associates in water. Inorganic carbon exists in water in a number of forms. When CO_2 is dissolved in water, most remains as $CO_2(aq)$ (usually represented as carbonic acid, H_2CO_3), but a smaller amount is present as hydrogen carbonate ions (HCO_3^-) produced by dissociation of H_2CO_3:

$$CO_2(g) + H_2O(l) = H_2CO_3(aq) = H^+(aq) + HCO_3^-(aq) \qquad (4.1)$$

and at higher pH, the hydrogen carbonate ion dissociates further, to give a carbonate ion (CO_3^{2-}):

$$HCO_3^-(aq) = CO_3^{2-}(aq) + H^+(aq) \qquad (4.2)$$

Hence, it is the concentration of H^+ in solution (i.e. pH) that determines the relative proportions of the different dissolved inorganic carbon compounds (CO_2, HCO_3^- and CO_3^{2-}) in water. Low pH (below about 5) prevents the formation of ions from dissolved CO_2. Higher pH (7 to 8) favours the formation of hydrogen carbonate, HCO_3^-, whereas a pH above 9 favours the formation of carbonate, CO_3^{2-}. Collectively, the assemblage of inorganic and organic carbon becomes the runoff carbon flux.

ph high

Rejoining the journey of our carbon atom, we see that soil organic matter and further particulate material from rivers (e.g. remains of leaves, dead freshwater plankton) accumulates in estuaries or nearshore sediments, from where the carbon may be released to the overlying water through biological oxidation. Some material escapes oxidation and is buried.

○ So far, in the journey of our carbon atom, which sites have been identified as likely environments where carbon can escape the terrestrial carbon cycle by being buried?

● Organic accumulations on land and similar accumulations in estuaries and nearshore sediments.

These land and near-land deposits account for the removal of a small amount of carbon from the terrestrial carbon cycle into the longer-term geological carbon cycle. However, if our carbon atom escapes burial, its next destination is the ocean and the intermediate time-scale marine carbon cycle.

4.2 Intermediate time-scales: the marine carbon cycle

When our carbon atom enters the ocean, it enters a biogeochemical environment with few similarities to the one it has just left. The dominant photosynthetic organisms in the surface ocean are the free-floating phytoplankton (Figure 4.3). These organisms include diatoms (microscopic phytoplankton with silica shells) and coccolithophores, which are microscopic phytoplankton that secrete calcareous plates over their surface. These algae occupy the uppermost sunlit 100 m or so of the ocean, known as the **photic zone**. Phytoplankton consume CO_2 and release O_2 through photosynthesis, in much the same way that land plants do; the only difference is that the gases used and produced are dissolved in seawater. Much of the organic matter produced in the surface ocean by phytoplankton is consumed by free-floating consumers called zooplankton, which include small invertebrates and microbes such as foraminifera (microbes with calcareous shells) and radiolaria (marine planktonic animals with silica skeletons). Zooplankton produce faecal pellets and, together with other large organic particles, these can sink to great depths. During its passage to the deep ocean, however, marine organic matter is decomposed as it settles through the water column, releasing CO_2. Only around 1% of this organic matter reaches the sea-bed intact (Figure 4.4). Once incorporated in the sediment, degradation continues as aerobic and anaerobic organisms reduce the amount preserved to 0.1% of the original surface water organic matter. This 0.1% is a small proportion, but is another important leak in the system that allows carbon to enter the long-term geological carbon cycle.

Figure 4.3 Planktonic organisms. Diatoms (a) and coccolithophores (b) are phytoplankton. Foraminifera (c) and radiolaria (d) are zooplankton.

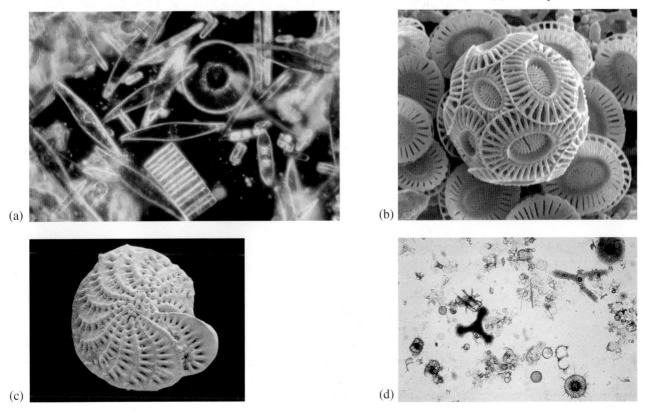

(a)

(b)

(c)

(d)

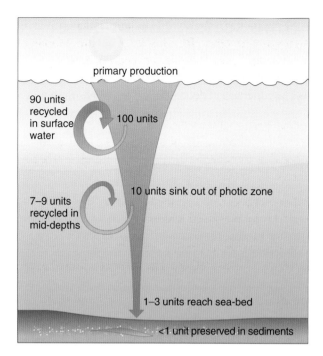

Figure 4.4 The progressive decrease with depth of the carbon initially fixed in the photic zone. Organic carbon is recycled as it descends through the water column and eventually less than 1% is preserved in sediments.

○ If the transport of photosynthetically produced organic matter to the deep ocean were to continue in isolation, what would be the consequence?

● The surface waters would eventually be stripped of dissolved CO_2.

However, there is a continuous exchange of gases between the atmosphere and ocean, and the CO_2 in surface waters is thereby replenished. The activity of phytoplankton can, therefore, affect the composition of the atmosphere as well as the ocean. The overall effect of the drawdown of CO_2 from the atmosphere, the photosynthetic fixation of CO_2 in surface waters, and the subsequent transport of the organic matter to deeper waters is known as the **biological pump**.

Another important biological process that uses carbon in seawater is the production of protective shells or skeletons. Many, though by no means all, organisms in the ocean have hard parts, as well as the soft tissues considered above. The ratio of organic (soft tissue) to inorganic (hard parts) carbon in plankton is generally 4 : 1. The hard parts are often composed of $CaCO_3$, which is made from hydrogen carbonate ions (HCO_3^-) and calcium ions (Ca^{2+}) obtained from seawater. As mentioned earlier, two important examples of organisms that secrete $CaCO_3$ are the phytoplanktonic coccolithophores and the zooplanktonic foraminifera. Radiolaria secrete silica, while other organisms utilize phosphates or any of a range of minor minerals.

When plankton die, their shells and skeletons sink though the water column and are not degraded as easily as organic matter. Generally, if the sea floor is at a depth of less than 4 km then the remains settle on the sea-bed, to be buried. Some of this eventually becomes carbonate rock. In shallow nearshore waters, bivalves such as mussels and oysters often grow together, forming large accumulations of $CaCO_3$ shells and in clear tropical waters certain algae form carbonate-rich accumulations, while coral skeletons build up to form substantial reefs. In deeper environments, the water is CO_2-rich due to the decomposition of organic matter.

○ CO_2 is more soluble in water at lower temperatures and higher pressures. How will this property affect the concentration of dissolved CO_2 in deep ocean waters? (*Hint*: deep ocean waters are at lower temperatures and higher pressures than surface waters.)

● The lower temperatures and higher pressures in deep ocean waters will allow them to hold more dissolved CO_2 than surface waters.

If we recall that CO_2 dissolved in water forms carbonic acid, then we can predict that this water will be acidic and corrosive to $CaCO_3$. The level at which the rate of dissolution of $CaCO_3$ is equal to the flux of material through the water column is called the **carbonate compensation depth** and below this depth, all shells dissolve. It is for this reason that the deep ocean floor has no $CaCO_3$ sediments. Figure 4.5 reveals that $CaCO_3$ sediments are restricted to topographically high areas such as the mid-ocean ridges.

So far, we have imagined the oceans to be a two-dimensional water column, but in reality the oceans are three-dimensional and involve a large-scale circulation, which can help to introduce and remove CO_2 from deep ocean waters (Box 4.1).

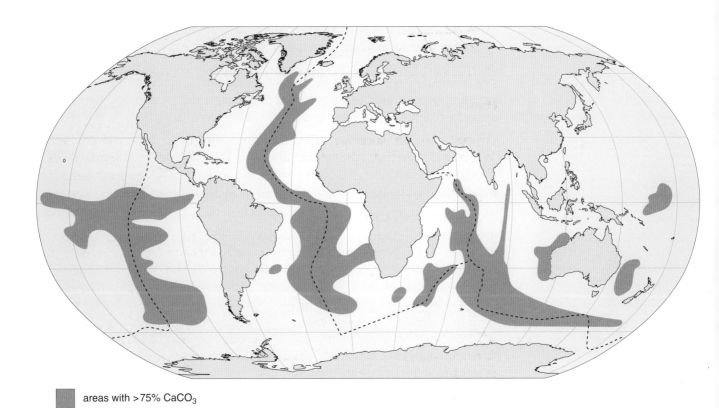

areas with >75% $CaCO_3$

Figure 4.5 The distribution of $CaCO_3$-rich ocean floor sediments. The dashed lines represent mid-ocean ridge systems.

Box 4.1 Coming in from the cold

Deep ocean waters originate in high latitudes where cooling of surface waters and the formation of sea ice (which leaves the residual water more saline) increases water density, causing it to sink. These cool waters can hold relatively large amounts of dissolved CO_2 and so deep ocean waters tend to be CO_2-rich to start with. Figure 4.6 is a cross-section of the Atlantic Ocean, which shows how CO_2 is transported through the deep ocean by currents. Once in the deep ocean, the CO_2 content of the water is supplemented by decomposing organic matter supplied from directly above by the biological pump. Note how NADW eventually returns to the surface and its load of dissolved CO_2 is released to the atmosphere.

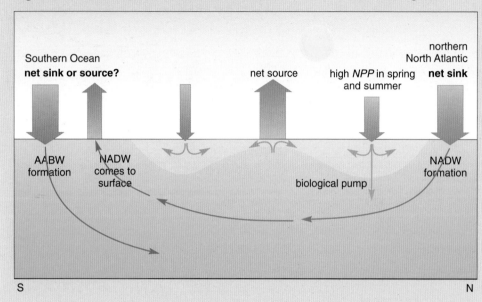

Figure 4.6 Cross-section of the Atlantic Ocean showing how cold high-latitude waters act as sinks for CO_2. These waters then sink and transport this CO_2 to the deep ocean. Deep ocean waters eventually resurface and release their dissolved CO_2 to the atmosphere. NADW is the North Atlantic Deep Water, AABW is Antarctic Bottom Water.

Figure 4.6 illustrates that the deep ocean waters are not an endless sink for CO_2; oceanic circulation eventually brings CO_2-rich deep waters back to the surface. In upwelling regions, the CO_2 passes from the ocean to the atmosphere. Hence there are net fluxes of CO_2 both into and out of the ocean, with areas of deep water formation and areas of high productivity, where there are flourishing planktonic populations acting as sinks, and areas of upwelling deep CO_2-rich waters acting as sources of atmospheric CO_2 (Figure 4.7).

Now that we have explored the marine carbon cycle, we can add this component to our terrestrial carbon cycle. Figure 4.8 shows how these two subcycles link together.

○ What is the largest reservoir in the combined terrestrial and marine carbon cycle?

● The deep ocean is by far the largest reservoir with $38\,000 \times 10^{12}\,kg\,C$ at any one time.

The remaining reservoirs in the marine carbon cycle are the surface waters ($1000 \times 10^{12}\,kg\,C$) and the sea-bed sediments ($3000 \times 10^{12}\,kg\,C$).

We have mentioned a number of 'leaks' in our short-term terrestrial and intermediate-term marine carbon cycle that result in carbon being buried. These leaks enter the geosphere to become part of the long-term geological carbon cycle. We will assume that our carbon atom has escaped degradation in the water column and become buried in marine sediments. We will now follow its progress through the long-term geological carbon cycle.

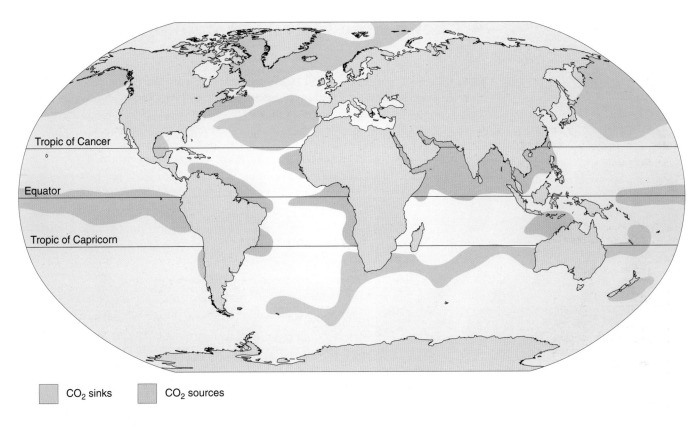

Figure 4.7 Areas of the oceans that act as sources and sinks of atmospheric CO_2.

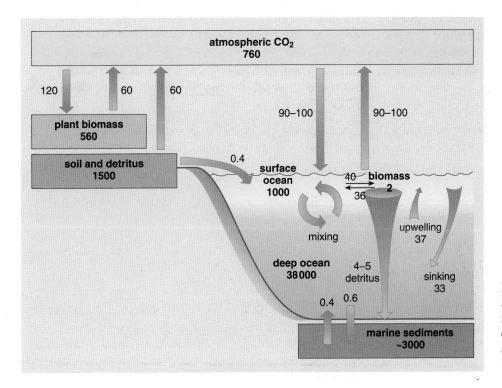

Figure 4.8 The combined marine and terrestrial carbon cycle. All reservoirs (bold values) are expressed in units of 10^{12} kg C and annual fluxes in units of 10^{12} kg C yr^{-1}.

4.3 Long time-scales: the geological carbon cycle

Over long time periods, a small fraction of carbon from the terrestrial and marine carbon cycles accumulates within sediments and is removed into longer-term storage. There are two different types of carbon-rich accumulations: sediments containing carbonate (carbon in inorganic form), and those containing organic remains.

Figure 4.9 Calcareous rocks: chalk cliffs at Beachy Head, Sussex, UK, composed of the remains of coccolithophores.

The first of these types of sediment is described as calcareous (Figure 4.9). These sediments are generally marine deposits containing accumulations of $CaCO_3$ shells and skeletons, which have been made by organisms using dissolved inorganic carbon. Over millions of years, chemical and structural changes occur in the sediments and they become rocks such as chalk and limestone. Calcareous material accumulates in the ocean at a rate of $0.2 \times 10^{12}\,\text{kg C yr}^{-1}$ and at any one time the reservoir of carbonate rock contains $40\,000\,000 \times 10^{12}\,\text{kg C}$.

The second kind of carbon-rich accumulation, containing organic material, is often described as **carbonaceous** (Figure 4.10). As organic-rich material is covered with more organic matter and sediment, the weight of the overlying deposits causes compaction, squeezing out water and residual air from the pore spaces. In the resulting oxygen-poor environment, a dense residue enriched in carbon is formed. Under continued deposition of organic matter and sediments, the original material may be buried to depths of several kilometres. As in the case of calcareous remains, high temperatures and pressures eventually cause the sediments to become lithified. Large accumulations of land plants may become coal, and marine sediments containing very high concentrations of phytoplankton debris can produce petroleum-source rocks. On land and sea, $0.05 \times 10^{12}\,\text{kg C yr}^{-1}$ is deposited as buried organic matter and at any one time there is a reservoir of $10\,000\,000 \times 10^{12}\,\text{kg C}$.

Figure 4.10 Carbonaceous rocks: cliffs at Kimmeridge Bay, Dorset, UK.

○ What is the ratio of the mass of carbon in calcareous rocks to the mass of carbon in carbonaceous rocks on Earth?

● $40\,000\,000 \times 10^{12}$ kg : $10\,000\,000 \times 10^{12}$ kg, or 4 : 1.

Rocks form by far the greatest carbon reservoir on Earth — as indicated in Figure 4.11, approximately 50×10^{18} kg C is locked up in them for periods of around 100 to 200 million years. However, the geological carbon cycle is a *cycle* and, eventually, this carbon does return to the Earth's atmosphere. One of the ways in which this happens is via the exposure and weathering of rock. Mountain-building pushes deeply buried carbon-containing rocks up to, or close to, the surface and exposes them to oxidation by atmospheric oxygen or oxygen dissolved in groundwaters. The inevitable consequence of this process is that the carbon is transformed back to CO_2 and the cycle can begin again.

So we now know that carbon can be locked up in the geosphere, for extended lengths of time, before being released back to the atmosphere. But what is less obvious is that the process of organic carbon burial can have a significant effect on the composition of the Earth's atmosphere. Refer back to the equations for photosynthesis and respiration (Section 3.1). The oxygen removed from the atmosphere during respiration is balanced by that released during photosynthesis, so as long as no organic matter is removed from the system, the atmospheric oxygen levels will remain the same. However, if organic matter is buried, the situation is different. Burial of organic carbon produced by photosynthesis excludes it from taking part in respiration and so the balance is disturbed.

Figure 4.11 The natural global carbon cycle. All reservoirs (bold values) are expressed in units of 10^{12} kg C and annual fluxes in units of 10^{12} kg C yr^{-1}.

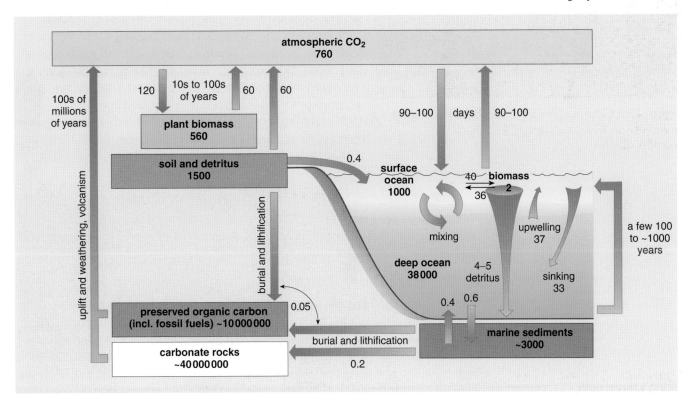

○ What is the net result to the atmosphere of organic matter burial?

● For every carbon atom that enters the rock reservoir, one oxygen molecule is left behind.

Look again at Figure 4.10 and the dark organic-rich rocks at Kimmeridge Bay. Now imagine just how much oxygen has been released into the atmosphere because of the incarceration of the organic products of photosynthesis in the geosphere. Then expand this thought to encompass those organic-rich rocks exposed in other parts of the world and similar rocks that are buried beneath the Earth's surface. It is then possible to appreciate that it is the geological process of organic carbon burial, over millions of years, that has flooded our atmosphere with oxygen.

A further important geological process that is responsible for controlling atmospheric composition is the weathering of rocks. Carbonate rocks are weathered on land but the products of weathering are also used to precipitate carbonate in the ocean. Examine the two equations below:

Carbonate weathering:

$$CaCO_3 + CO_2 + H_2O = Ca^{2+} + 2HCO_3^- \tag{4.3}$$

Carbonate precipitation:

$$Ca^{2+} + 2HCO_3^- = CaCO_3 + H_2CO_3 \tag{4.4}$$

○ What is the net result of the carbonate weathering and precipitation reactions? (Remember that H_2CO_3 is equivalent to $CO_2 + H_2O$.)

● The net result is no change.

You can see that the equation for carbonate weathering is the opposite of that for carbonate precipitation, so there is a balance between the weathering of $CaCO_3$ on land and precipitating the same mineral in the oceans. Silicate weathering is, however, different. In the following equations, we represent silicates by the mineral wollastonite ($CaSiO_3$).

Silicate weathering:

$$CaSiO_3 + 2CO_2 + H_2O = Ca^{2+} + 2HCO_3^- + SiO_2 \tag{4.5}$$

Carbonate precipitation:

$$Ca^{2+} + 2HCO_3^- = CaCO_3 + H_2CO_3 \tag{4.6}$$

Adding these two equations together, we see that the net result of silicate weathering and carbonate precipitation is the removal of one CO_2 molecule from the atmosphere for each $CaSiO_3$ unit removed:

$$CaSiO_3 + CO_2 = CaCO_3 + SiO_2 \tag{4.7}$$

Thus the combined process of silicate weathering on land and carbonate precipitation in the oceans leads to a net loss of CO_2 from the atmosphere. The carbonate and silicate weathering and carbonate precipitation reactions are displayed diagrammatically in Figure 4.12. Incidentally, the dissolved SiO_2 left over from this reaction is utilized in the production of shells for the radiolaria we encountered earlier when discussing marine planktonic organisms.

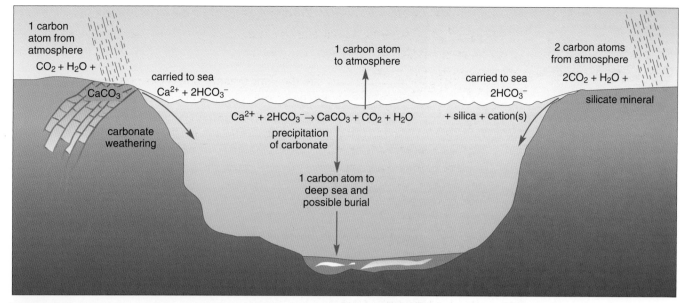

Figure 4.12   A summary diagram of the weathering of carbonate and silicate rocks on land and the deposition of carbonate in the ocean.

○   What is the implication for the atmosphere of organic carbon burial and silicate weathering on land?

●   Carbon 'leaks' out of the atmospheric reservoir and into the rock reservoir.

The weathering of silicate rock has been removing CO_2 from the Earth's atmosphere for millions of years but today's atmosphere still contains CO_2. Consequently, to complete our long-term geochemical carbon cycle and liberate the carbon atom whose journey we have been following, we need a mechanism in which buried carbon is released. Plate tectonics fulfils this need. At plate margins, carbon-containing sediments are subducted and subjected to high temperatures and pressures and CO_2 is reintroduced to the atmosphere through volcanoes (Figure 2.5). This 'global conveyor belt' (Figure 2.2) recycles the whole oceanic crust over time-scales of hundreds of millions of years.

4.4 Short-circuiting the geological carbon cycle

In the long-term, the carbon cycle is in balance, with inputs to the atmosphere balanced by outputs to the biosphere and geosphere. But in very recent years the carbon cycle has been disturbed: today there is more carbon entering the atmosphere than there is being removed. In other words, inputs exceed outputs and the atmospheric reservoir of carbon is growing by around $3 \times 10^{12} \, \text{kg} \, \text{C} \, \text{yr}^{-1}$.

This situation became clear when, in 1957, Charles Keeling set up a station for the continuous monitoring of CO_2 in the atmosphere. The location was a 4300 m high volcano in Hawaii called Mauna Loa (Figure 4.13). The volcano was far from sources of atmospheric pollution and right in the path of clean air blowing across the Pacific Ocean. Keeling's measurements showed that the CO_2 concentration of the atmosphere in Hawaii averaged around 317 parts per million

Figure 4.13 The observatory at Mauna Loa, Hawaii.

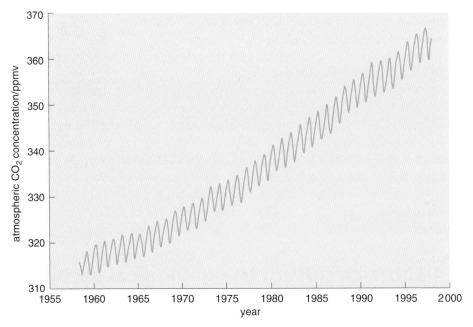

Figure 4.14 The record of atmospheric CO_2 collected at Mauna Loa, Hawaii.

by volume (ppmv), but oscillated around that value over the year, increasing in the winter and decreasing in the summer, reflecting the growth of terrestrial biomass in the Northern Hemisphere summer (Figure 4.14).

Question 4.2

Look at Figure 4.14 and answer the following questions.
(a) Ignoring the seasonal oscillations, identify the longer-term trend of CO_2 concentrations. (b) By about how much (in ppmv) have atmospheric CO_2 concentrations risen between 1958 and 1998?

Within about five years after the establishment of monitoring stations, it had become obvious that the annual average atmospheric CO_2 concentration was steadily increasing. No natural phenomenon could be found to account for this spectacularly rapid rate of increase. So when did this increase begin? The answer to this question was sought in ice cores that were drilled in the summer of 1982–1983 at the Vostock base on the high plateau of the Antarctic ice-cap. The age of the ice down the core could be determined by counting the number of annual layers of snow accumulation. Moreover, crucially, each year as the ice accumulated, air bubbles were trapped within the ice (Figure 4.15). Analyses of air trapped in ice cores revealed that the current rapid increase in atmospheric CO_2 began approximately 100 years ago, and has greatly accelerated in recent decades (Figure 4.16).

But what is the cause of the increase in atmospheric CO_2 concentrations? By far the most plausible explanation is the extraction and burning of fossil fuels and deforestation which release carbon from the long-term stores much more rapidly than would occur naturally. Thus, human activities short-circuit the geological carbon cycle (Figure 4.17).

Figure 4.15 The collection of ice cores at Vostok, Antarctica.

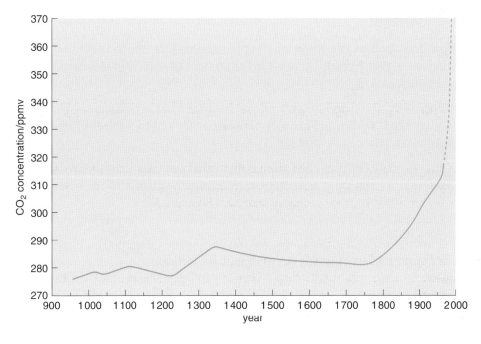

Figure 4.16 The record of atmospheric CO_2 over the last 1000 years from ice core records (solid line) and direct atmospheric measurements (dashed line).

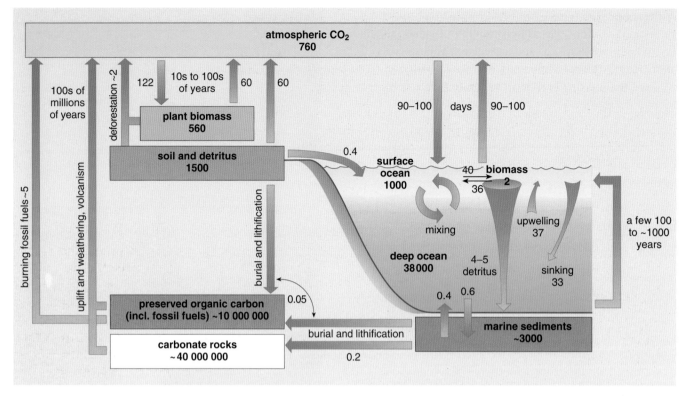

Figure 4.17   Summary diagram of the carbon cycle, which now includes the burning of fossil fuels.

The important point here is not the fact that carbon is being returned to the atmosphere (this would eventually happen anyway), but the *rate* at which this process is occurring. Concentrations of CO_2 in the atmosphere are increasing faster than fluxes into the other reservoirs can accommodate them. Because the increase in atmospheric CO_2 levels is primarily due to fossil fuel use, we can make accurate estimates of the flux of carbon being added to the atmosphere. According to global production figures for coal and oil, it is approximately 5×10^{12} kg C yr^{-1}.

○   How does the flux of carbon entering the atmosphere due to fossil fuel use compare with the yearly increase in the amount of carbon in the atmospheric reservoir?

●   Surprisingly, the current yearly rate of increase of CO_2 in the atmosphere (3×10^{12} kg C yr^{-1}, p.145) is only between a half and two-thirds of that being added from fossil fuels (5×10^{12} kg C yr^{-1}).

It appears, therefore, that not all of the CO_2 generated by burning fossil fuels is staying in the atmosphere and there is a sink for the carbon.

○   By reference to Figure 4.17, suggest possible sinks for the missing carbon.

●   The only possibilities to account for the discrepancy seem to be either the ocean or plant biomass (terrestrial or marine, or both).

An increase in the concentration of atmospheric CO_2 will cause an increase in the flux of CO_2 into the ocean; computer models of ocean circulation and calculations of carbonate equilibria suggest that an extra 1.6×10^{12} kg C yr^{-1}

could eventually be removed from the atmosphere to the oceans in this way. Increased rates of fixation of carbon in plant material is another possibility. Small-scale experiments have shown that an increase in the concentration of atmospheric CO_2 actually has a fertilizing effect on plant growth, thus storing some of the missing carbon in vegetation or soil organic matter.

The rise of the Earth's atmospheric CO_2 levels has attracted great attention due to the possible climatic effects, such as increased global warming and an associated sea-level rise as the world's store of glacial ice begins to melt. Efforts have been made to model the future rise in CO_2 to inform policy decisions that mitigate against climatic change (Box 4.2).

Box 4.2 Onwards and upwards—the future of atmospheric CO_2

Working groups of the Intergovernmental Panel on Climate Change (IPCC) have made a series of projections on the effects of **anthropogenic** CO_2 emissions (those produced as a result of human activity) on the Earth's atmosphere. These emissions result not only from fossil fuel use, but also from deforestation. Like any future predictions, the models contain a level of uncertainty.

Figure 4.18a displays several of the scenarios computed in the 2001 Special Report on Emission Scenarios that may occur. All A1 scenarios assume rapid economic growth and technological development.

- A1FI is the highest emission curve, reflecting intensive fossil fuel use.

- A1T represents a shift to non-fossil energy sources.

- A1B is the curve for the use of balanced energy sources.

- B1 reflects an economic change towards the introduction of clean and resource-efficient technologies.

When these scenarios are used to calculate future atmospheric concentrations of CO_2, striking predictions are generated (Figure 4.18b). By 2100, CO_2 levels have soared to 700 ppmv in the mid-range A1B case. Even in the most optimistic B1 scenario, the atmospheric CO_2 concentration is above 500 ppmv. Doubling or tripling the concentration of CO_2 in the atmosphere would have significant and currently unpredictable environmental effects on the Earth. Clearly, a thorough understanding of the internal working of the carbon cycle will stand the human race in good stead for determining the causes and consequences of future changes in atmospheric CO_2.

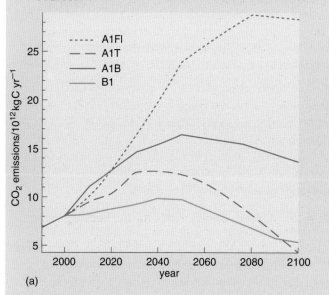

(a)

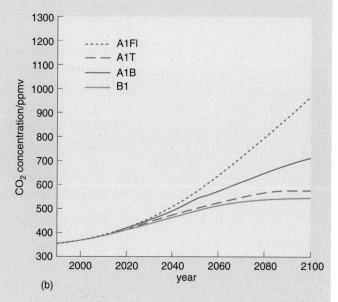

(b)

Figure 4.18   (a) Predicted anthropogenic emissions of CO_2, and (b) future atmospheric CO_2 concentrations based on the IPCC 2001 Special Report on Emission Scenarios.

Question 4.3

If, due to fossil fuel use, atmospheric CO_2 levels continue to rise, how do you think this will affect the carbonate compensation depth and the distribution of ocean-floor carbonate sediments in Figure 4.5? (Remember from Section 4.3 that atmospheric CO_2 dissolves in seawater.)

We should not leave the carbon cycle without mentioning another component, the gas methane (CH_4). Atmospheric CH_4 concentration (1.75 ppmv) is much less than that of CO_2 (360 ppmv). However, each molecule of CH_4 in the atmosphere has the potential to create 25 times as much greenhouse warming as each molecule of CO_2, and over the last several decades the concentration of CH_4 has been increasing by about 1% per year, much faster than CO_2 (Figure 4.16). Methane is emitted from swamps, wetlands, rice paddies and cattle, and is the principal constituent of the natural gas many of us use for domestic heating, and substantial amounts are lost during extraction of fossil fuels. Yet the residence time of methane is short and it is oxidized to CO_2 in less than 10 years.

Question 4.4

Why will the carbon atoms contained in CH_4 continue to take part in greenhouse warming after the CH_4 has been destroyed by oxidation?

Question 4.5

If the marine biological pump suddenly began to transport twice as much organic debris to the ocean floor, much of which became incorporated into sediments and ultimately rock, would atmospheric oxygen levels increase or decrease?

4.5 Summary of Section 4

1. The global carbon cycle involves processes in the atmosphere, on the land and in the sea. Both biological and non-biological reactions take place.

2. The global carbon cycle can be divided into three subcycles, each of which operates on a different time-scale. The terrestrial carbon cycle operates on a time-scale of months to decades, the marine carbon cycle operates over hundreds of thousands of years, and the geological carbon cycle operates over millions of years.

3. The terrestrial carbon cycle operates on short time-scales. Carbon dioxide is removed from the atmosphere and photosynthesis transforms it into organic compounds. Some carbon is returned to the atmosphere quickly via respiration while the rest becomes organic matter. When a plant dies, the carbon is incorporated into the soil and microbial degradation releases it as CO_2. A small amount of carbon escapes respiration and decomposition and is buried on land or transported by runoff to the oceans.

4. The marine carbon cycle operates on intermediate time-scales. Marine phytoplankton utilize dissolved CO_2 in surface waters to generate organic matter, which eventually sinks down through the water column. The CO_2 in surface waters is replenished from the atmosphere and this transport of carbon to the deep ocean constitutes the biological pump. As with the terrestrial carbon cycle, small amounts of organic matter escape degradation and are buried in sediments.

5   The small but steady leak of carbon from the terrestrial and marine carbon cycles due to burial allows carbon to enter the geological carbon cycle. This cycle operates on long time-scales and the rock reservoirs contain most of the carbon in the carbon cycle. This carbon is returned to the atmosphere and ocean when tectonic processes expose buried carbon to be weathered or directly oxidized to CO_2.

6   Over the last 100 years, the concentration of CO_2 in the atmosphere has been rising. This rise is caused primarily by the burning of fossil fuels. Fossil fuel use short-circuits the geological carbon cycle by increasing the rate of transfer between the geospheric and atmospheric carbon reservoirs.

Learning outcomes for Section 4

After working through this section you should be able to:

4.1 Explain how the global carbon cycle consists of a number of subcycles and that these subcycles operate on varying time-scales. (*Question 4.1*)

4.2 Calculate residence times for the main reservoirs of carbon on the Earth. (*Question 4.1*)

4.3 Describe the processes that transfer carbon between the various reservoirs. (*Questions 4.3 and 4.5*)

4.4 Recognize the respective roles of biology and geology in the carbon cycle. (*Questions 4.3 and 4.5*)

4.5 Describe the effect of human intervention in the carbon cycle. (*Questions 4.2–4.4*)

5

The nitrogen cycle

5.1 The global nitrogen cycle

A simple representation of the global nitrogen cycle is shown in Figure 5.1. In contrast to the carbon cycle, the global nitrogen cycle is not truly global at all, but a series of linked ecosystems. This is a concept we explore further below.

N_2 dinitrogen
N_2O Nitrous oxide
NO Nitric oxide
NO_2 Nitrogen dioxide
NO_3^- Nitrate
NH_3 - Amonia
NH_4 - Ammonium

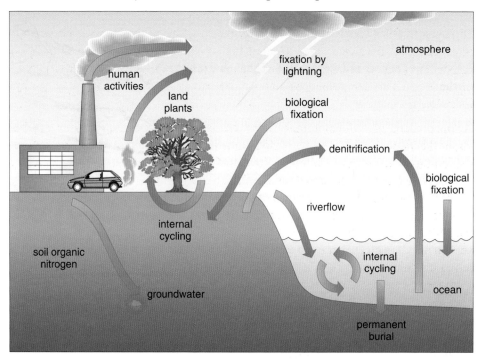

Figure 5.1 The present-day 'global' nitrogen cycle.

The largest reservoir of nitrogen is the atmosphere (3.8×10^{18} kg N). Atmospheric nitrogen is predominantly in the form of the diatomic molecule N_2. Although N_2 is commonly referred to as nitrogen or nitrogen gas, it should be more correctly referred to as dinitrogen, a term indicating its molecular composition. The two nitrogen atoms in the N_2 molecule are joined by a very strong triple bond.

○ If dinitrogen dominates the atmosphere, why might the availability of nitrogen often be a limiting factor in plant growth?

● The strong triple bond is a major factor in the low reactivity of the N_2 molecule. Plants require nitrogen in a form that can be used for the synthesis of proteins.

For dinitrogen to be used by plants, it has to be converted into a usable form, or 'fixed'. For this to occur, the triple bond has to be broken during **nitrogen fixation** reactions, which involve either hydrogen or oxygen. Nitrogen fixation can be achieved in one of two naturally occurring ways: firstly, via biological nitrogen fixation, where dinitrogen combines with hydrogen from water, and the ultimate product is the ammonium cation, NH_4^+; secondly, during lightning strikes, where dinitrogen combines with atmospheric oxygen, O_2, and the ultimate product is the nitrate anion, NO_3^-. Both of these inorganic nitrogen-containing ions can be assimilated by plants, although NO_3^- is converted to NH_4^+ by the plants themselves. Chemical species such as NH_4^+ and NO_3^- can collectively be termed **biologically active nitrogen** because they can readily be incorporated by all plants, unlike dinitrogen, which can be considered to be biologically inactive. The common term for biologically active nitrogen is **fixed nitrogen**.

○ What common farming practice suggests that the abundant pool of atmospheric dinitrogen cannot be used directly by most plants?

● The use of nitrogen-containing fertilizers in the production of food crops and animal fodder.

Nitrogen fixation is one of the most important aspects of the biogeochemical nitrogen cycle, because it can influence the amount of food present within an ecosystem. Indeed, natural nitrogen fixation cannot meet the food requirements of the world's human population and it is necessary to fix additional nitrogen by industrial processes.

At the present time, the amount of nitrogen fixed by industrial processes may be about the same as that fixed by biological activity, although the exact figures are difficult to estimate. For example, nitrogen-fixing organisms are microscopic, not all have been characterized, and their activity depends upon the chemical characteristics and the temperature of the environments in which they live. Even in a small area of temperate grassland, the chemical characteristics will be highly variable, notably with soil depth, and the temperature changes both daily and seasonally. It is clear that even getting an approximate answer for the annual amount of nitrogen fixation in a small field would be fraught with difficulties. Imagine trying to get an estimate for global nitrogen fixation, where one has to consider every marine, terrestrial and freshwater environment. Similarly, in order to estimate the amount of nitrogen being fixed industrially, one would have to obtain the production figures for every industrial plant in every country, which again would not be an easy task.

Because nitrogen fixation is so important, we shall consider this as a separate topic, before examining the cycling of nitrogen in a temperate grassland.

5.2 Nitrogen fixation: the reasons why

5.2.1 The 'global ecosystem'

The schematic diagram of Figure 5.2 indicates why nitrogen fixation is necessary for the functioning of the biosphere on a global scale.

Averaged over time, the amount of biomass present within the biosphere can be considered to be constant. This constant amount of biomass will be supported by a constant level of fixed nitrogen of all forms, and we shall call this level the 'optimum value'. It is worth remembering this concept of an optimum value of fixed nitrogen, as we will return to it repeatedly throughout this section. However, during the cycling of nitrogen, a significant amount of nitrate, NO_3^-, is converted back to dinitrogen (and minor amounts of two oxides of nitrogen, N_2O and NO) by a bacterial process known as **denitrification**.

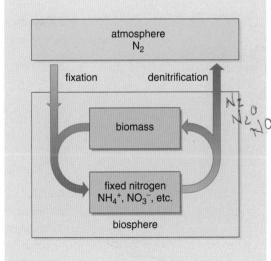

Figure 5.2 Fixation of dinitrogen in the 'global ecosystem'.

○ If denitrification occurred in isolation, how would it affect the levels of fixed nitrogen in an ecosystem?

● Denitrification would cause levels of fixed nitrogen to fall.

If denitrification were the only major process operating in the biogeochemical nitrogen cycle, then the levels of fixed nitrogen would decline so rapidly that the biosphere would cease to function in less than 200 years. Common experience tells us that this is not the case, and the losses due to denitrification are balanced by a process that replenishes fixed nitrogen.

○ Look at Figure 5.2 and suggest a mechanism for the replenishment of fixed nitrogen.

● The biological fixation of atmospheric N_2.

To understand how nitrogen fixation occurs, we need to examine the cycling of nitrogen on a more local scale.

5.2.2   The fixation of nitrogen on a more local scale

Global schemes such as that in Figure 5.2 are useful to introduce the basic aspects of the nitrogen cycle. However, they hide the fact that the global system is simply an integration of a multitude of smaller ecosystems that are interrelated. Figure 5.3 represents a subsystem in the global biosphere involving a lake surrounded by soils.

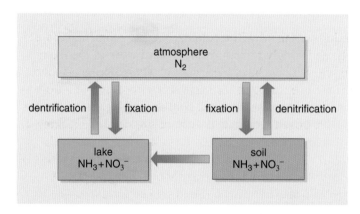

Figure 5.3   The fixation of nitrogen on a more local scale.

Nitrogen fixation and denitrification will be occurring in both the lake and soil environments, and if each environment were totally closed, then nitrogen fixation would exactly balance the losses due to denitrification (similar to Figure 5.2).

○ Are the soil and lake environments in Figure 5.3 acting as individual closed systems?

● No they are open systems. Nitrogen will be lost from the soils, and transported to the lake.

The consequence of this open system is that the fine balance between nitrogen fixation and denitrification will be disturbed in both the soils and the lake. Large amounts of NO_3^- and NH_3 can be lost from soils by processes known as **nitrate**

leaching and **ammonia volatilization** respectively, and some of this fixed nitrogen could be washed into the lake, for example (Figure 5.3).

On the global scale, this simply represents a redistribution of fixed nitrogen, and the overall level stays at the optimum value. However, on the more local scale we have a situation where the levels of fixed nitrogen are falling below their optimum value in the soils, and rising above their optimum value in the lake, a situation that has biogeochemical consequences for both environments. We will now focus on each individual environment and explore these consequences.

Soil

Consider a hypothetical situation where the soils have lost all of their fixed nitrogen. Even if all of the other nutrients were present, this would still represent a sterile environment for most organisms. However, living organisms are opportunists, and in the geological past, certain bacteria evolved that were capable of exploiting such situations. Today, these nitrogen-fixing organisms are capable of detecting when the levels of fixed nitrogen fall below the optimum value, and when this occurs, nitrogen-fixing genes (*nif* genes) are activated. The activation of these *nif* genes initiates biochemical and physiological changes that convert the organisms into mini nitrogen-fixing factories, allowing them to thrive in an otherwise sterile environment.

○ What is the consequence of the activity of nitrogen-fixing organisms?

● The levels of fixed nitrogen in soils will be brought back up towards their optimum value.

When this occurs, non-fixing organisms will recolonize the environment, because they are also opportunists, and simply benefit from the hard work of the fixers. Now, in our hypothetical scenario, we have the situation where nitrogen-fixing and non-fixing organisms are coexisting in the same soil. However, the nitrogen-fixing organisms would now be at a distinct ecological disadvantage. Remember that the triple bond of the dinitrogen molecule is very strong, and the breaking of this bond requires a lot of energy. During nitrogen fixation, energy that could have been used for plant growth, for example, is diverted towards the breaking of the triple bond of dinitrogen. Non-fixing organisms simply assimilate fixed nitrogen, in which the N≡N bonds have already been broken for them, hence more of their energy can be used directly for plant growth. So, in order to remain competitive when the levels of fixed nitrogen have been brought back to the optimum value, the nitrogen-fixing organisms will cease the fixation of atmospheric dinitrogen and simply assimilate fixed nitrogen, like all of the other organisms.

Although nitrogen-fixing organisms can respond rapidly to changes in the levels of fixed nitrogen, these levels do not fluctuate greatly in natural ecosystems. You must not think that nitrogen-fixing organisms are continually switching on and off their capabilities in response to rapid changes in the optimum value of fixed nitrogen. In reality, there is a fine balance between the type of soil, the extent of nitrogen loss, and the ratio of active nitrogen-fixing to non-fixing organisms. This constant 'battle' for ecological supremacy between nitrogen-fixing and non-fixing organisms is one of the main reasons why the levels of fixed nitrogen in the global ecosystem remain relatively constant.

Lake

We have seen that nitrogen-fixing organisms can replenish nitrogen losses from soils, but what happens to the fixed nitrogen that is washed into a lake? Although we shall consider the processes in more detail later, the effect of adding fixed nitrogen to an ecosystem is the same as putting fertilizer on a field, where the whole of the cycle is 'speeded up', leading to a better yield of crops. Similarly, in a lake, the addition of fixed nitrogen simply enhances denitrification, and this will keep the levels of fixed nitrogen at the optimum value.

5.3 Nitrogen fixation: the mechanisms

Lightning strikes and biological nitrogen fixation are the two main processes of natural nitrogen fixation; however, in recent years the growth of intensive agriculture has prompted the development of industrial nitrogen fixation.

5.3.1 Lightning strikes

When a lightning strike cuts through the atmosphere, it causes intense heating of the atmospheric gases in its path, which is only about the width of a human thumb. Although the total duration of the strike is about 0.2 seconds, the temperature at peak intensity can reach 30 000 °C, which is about five times hotter than the surface of the Sun. During the intense heating that accompanies a lightning strike, sufficient energy is absorbed by the dinitrogen molecule to split the triple bond and produce nitrogen atoms. These atoms are highly reactive and can react with other atoms, molecules or ions. Some nitrogen atoms may collide with other nitrogen atoms to reform dinitrogen. However, a significant number will collide with oxygen atoms (produced by lightning-induced cleavage of oxygen molecules, O_2) or oxygen molecules. The result is the formation of nitric oxide, NO. Nitric oxide itself is reactive and will further combine with atmospheric O_2 to form nitrogen dioxide, NO_2. Both nitric oxide and nitrogen dioxide have significant solubility in water and dissolve in rain and cloud water to form nitrous and nitric acids (HNO_2 and HNO_3 respectively). The overall process can be represented by:

$$N_2 \xrightarrow{\text{lightning}} NO \longrightarrow NO_2 \longrightarrow HNO_2 \text{ and } HNO_3 \tag{5.1}$$

Both HNO_2 and HNO_3 will be deposited in the rains associated with thunderstorms, and both will dissociate, releasing biologically active NO_2^- and NO_3^- into marine, terrestrial and freshwater ecosystems. During biogeochemical cycling, NO_2^- is converted to NO_3^- through nitrification reactions. Therefore, lightning strikes contribute to the total pool of dissolved NO_3^- in ecosystems.

It has been estimated that at any one time there are about 2000 active thunderstorms over the surface of the planet, resulting in about 100 lightning strikes per second, and although figures vary, it appears that lightning strikes account for about 10% of the total annual amount of natural nitrogen fixation.

Question 5.1

Although the amount of nitrogen fixed by lightning strikes is insufficient for the needs of the biosphere, can you think of another ecological reason why the nitrogen fixed by lightning strikes may not be that important for modern ecosystems?

5.3.2 Natural biological nitrogen fixation

Both the amount and distribution of nitrogen fixed by lightning are insufficient for the needs of the modern biosphere. In the geological past, nitrogen-fixing organisms evolved that were able to exploit ecological niches in which nitrogen was the only limiting nutrient. We now examine nitrogen-fixing organisms in more detail.

Nitrogen-fixing organisms

The only confirmed free-living organisms that are capable of fixing nitrogen are certain bacteria, including free-living soil bacteria and cyanobacteria. Cyanobacteria are important nitrogen fixers in the oceans, although they are not found solely within the marine environment. Perhaps the most famous nitrogen-fixing organisms are bacteria of the genus *Rhizobium*, which enter into a symbiotic relationship with legumes (peas, beans, clover, etc.). A symbiotic relationship is a close association between two distinct species where both organisms benefit from the relationship.

Although these specialized organisms can fix atmospheric dinitrogen, their nitrogen-fixing capabilities may lie dormant if there is abundant fixed nitrogen in their immediate environment. For example, if a soil is rich in NH_4^+, then peas will thrive without requiring *Rhizobium* to fix atmospheric dinitrogen.

However, if the levels of fixed nitrogen start to fall, then the differences between nitrogen-fixing and non-fixing organisms become apparent. Non-fixing organisms will start to decline in direct proportion to the falling levels of fixed nitrogen, and there will be nothing that they can do about it. However, the specialized nitrogen-fixing organisms can 'detect' these falling nitrogen levels and, when a certain level is reached, the *nif* genes will be activated, and the organisms will start to fix atmospheric dinitrogen. In the case of legumes, it is the plant that detects the falling nitrogen levels, and it sends out a chemical signal from its roots, 'inviting' the *Rhizobium* to enter into a symbiotic relationship.

The activation of these *nif* genes provokes many changes in the organisms, from the synthesis of specialized proteins to pronounced morphological changes. For example, filamentous cyanobacteria such as *Anabaena* differentiate specialized nitrogen-fixing cells called heterocysts. However, more spectacular changes occur when *Rhizobium* enter into symbiotic relationships with legumes. In this case, there are two organisms that must fuse together to form a single working unit, requiring morphological changes to both. The outward expression of symbiosis is the development of nodules on the roots of the host plant (Figure 5.4). So, by simply examining the organism, one can see whether it is actively fixing dinitrogen. If you see clover growing in a sandy soil, carefully dig up the plant, and examine the roots. The presence of small nodules will reveal that the plant is actively fixing dinitrogen, and will also tell you something about the levels of fixed nitrogen in the soil.

Figure 5.4 Nodules on the roots of a legume.

Figure 5.5 Nitrogen-fixing lichen growing on bare rock.

○ Can you think of any environment on land where you would find only nitrogen-fixing organisms?

● Freshly exposed nitrogen-free rocks, such as lava flows or rocks that have recently been freed from glacial ice. The initial colonization of such rocks can be achieved only by nitrogen-fixing organisms.

Certain lichens are good examples of organisms that are capable of fixing nitrogen on bare rocks (see Figure 5.5). These are symbiotic relationships between fungal and algal partners, and if the algal partner is a cyanobacterium, then the lichen will be capable of fixing nitrogen. (Figure 4.11 in Block 3, Part 2, is a drawing of a lichen, showing a fungus with its cyanobacterial partner.)

Agriculture and the disruption of the 'natural order'

We have discussed how the constant 'battle' for ecological supremacy between nitrogen-fixing and non-fixing organisms maintains the levels of fixed nitrogen at the optimum value at both the local and global scale, and how in a temperate grassland there will be a fine balance between the soil environment, the levels of nitrogen loss, and the ratio of fixing to non-fixing organisms. Clearly, this fine balance will be seriously disrupted by agricultural practices.

For example, the diversity of plants found in a natural ecosystem may be reduced to a single crop, and that crop may be incapable of fixing nitrogen (such as wheat). If the crops cannot fix nitrogen, then natural losses of fixed nitrogen cannot be replenished. Furthermore, the losses of fixed nitrogen from soils are necessarily enhanced by agricultural practices, simply because the crops are removed from the fields, taking a lot of nitrogen that was originally in the soil with them. Obviously, the persistent planting and harvesting of wheat would eventually remove so much fixed nitrogen that the soils would lose their fertility.

This problem was recognized by farmers in ancient times, who would maintain the levels of fixed nitrogen by employing the practice of 'crop rotation'. Crop rotation involves changing the crop on a particular field each year and, most importantly, the planting of legumes (e.g. clover). In ancient times, fields would be left fallow for one year, allowing clover to grow for a sufficient time to restore the levels of fixed nitrogen. Clearly, this innovation was found by accident, because the ancient farmers could not have been aware of the biogeochemical principles involved.

Although crop rotation, aided by the recycling of animal wastes, was quite adequate for largely rural communities, the situation was to change markedly with industrialization, which resulted not only in a large population increase, but also in the growth of towns and cities.

5.3.3   Industrial nitrogen fixation

Importing animal and vegetable products from rural areas to urban areas necessarily implied a net loss of fixed nitrogen from agricultural soils. In the expanding urban areas, a lot of this imported nitrogen simply found its way into the sewers, and little (if any) was available for recycling in the fields of origin. Furthermore, it was no longer economically practical to leave fields fallow for protracted periods, and many of the crop plants were incapable of fixing nitrogen. Clearly, for agricultural production to keep pace with a rising population, highly concentrated, nitrogen-bearing fertilizers were required.

During the 19th century, it was possible to import naturally occurring fertilizers, notably from Latin America. Peru had large reserves of guano (bird-droppings) and, more importantly, Chile could supply nitrates, notably sodium nitrate ($NaNO_3$). Nitrates are important because they are strong oxidizing agents, and traditionally they have also been used in the manufacture of explosives, where oxygen from nitrates ($NaNO_3$, KNO_3) combines explosively with reduced materials such as a mixture of carbon and sulfur. Although people recognized that the supply of natural fertilizers had a limited lifetime, it was the dual usage of nitrates (agriculture and munitions) that was to provide the main stimulus for the development of industrial nitrogen fixation.

The first decade of the 20th century was a time of tension in Western Europe. In particular, Germany felt vulnerable, because the country's agricultural and munitions industries were reliant on steady supplies of nitrates from Latin America, which could have easily been cut off by a naval blockade. Accordingly, it was recognized that Germany had to become self-sufficient in nitrates. In 1909 a chemist called Fritz Haber provided the solution, and a chemical engineer, Carl Bosch, developed Haber's technique into a full working plant that went into production in 1913. War broke out the following year, and although German supplies of nitrates from Latin America were successfully stopped, the development of this Haber–Bosch process ensured German self-sufficiency in nitrates. Indeed, historians have argued that the First World War could not have been sustained without this technical innovation.

Although there have been refinements to the original Haber–Bosch process, the basic chemistry of industrial nitrogen fixation remains the same. Hydrogen gas derived from a fossil fuel, commonly from natural gas (CH_4), is combined with atmospheric dinitrogen at elevated temperatures and pressures, using nickel and iron as catalysts:

$$CH_4 + 2H_2O \xrightarrow{\text{Ni/750\,°C/30\,atm}} CO_2 + 4H_2 \tag{5.2}$$

$$N_2 + 3H_2 \xrightarrow{\text{Fe/400\,°C/200\,atm}} 2NH_3 \tag{5.3}$$

○ What is the most striking difference between industrial nitrogen fixation and biological nitrogen fixation?

● Whereas bacteria can fix nitrogen at ambient temperatures and pressures using sunlight as the energy source, industrial nitrogen fixation is energy-intensive, requiring both elevated temperatures and pressures.

Approximately 80% of the ammonia produced by the Haber–Bosch process is used for fertilizers — ammonia solutions are either applied directly to the fields, or incorporated into other compounds, such as urea $CO(NH_2)_2$, nitrates or ammonium salts, including ammonium sulfate, $(NH_4)_2SO_4$.

The application of fertilizers to fields highlights other major differences between biological and industrial nitrogen fixation. Biological nitrogen fixation is a direct response to biological needs. When applying fertilizers, a farmer has to make an educated guess as to how much nitrogen is required by the fields. Furthermore, in the symbiotic relationships in legumes, the biologically fixed nitrogen is incorporated directly into plant protein, whereas fertilizers are applied to the soils in the hope that the nitrogen will be assimilated by plants. However, fertilizers are actively cycled within the soil, before they can be assimilated by plants, which results in the formation of soluble inorganic and gaseous forms of nitrogen, which can be lost from the soils, and this can lead to problems of pollution. Indeed, as much as 50% of fertilizer nitrogen can be lost from soils, and the processes involved will be considered in the following sections.

5.4 The cycling of nitrogen within a temperate grassland

We are now in a position to examine the cycling of nitrogen within a single ecosystem. Because of its direct relevance to agriculture, we are going to consider a temperate grassland with a very restricted fauna and flora consisting of grass, clover and rabbits. Figure 5.6 shows the distribution of the various inorganic forms of nitrogen. In the following sections, we consider the major processes that result in the formation and removal of these inorganic species, and their relation to organic matter.

With any cycle, the choice of a starting point is somewhat arbitrary, but we shall begin by considering the inputs and outputs of nitrogen. This brief introduction simply applies what you have already learned to a particular case.

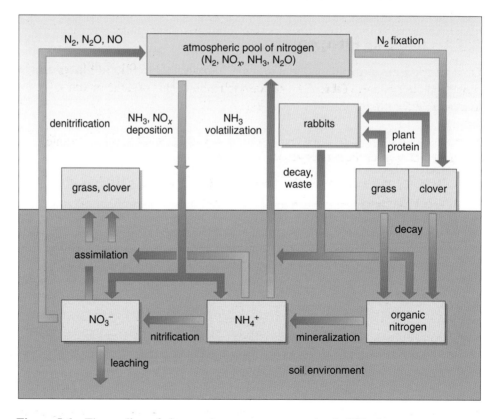

Figure 5.6   The cycling of nitrogen in a temperate grassland. (NO_x denotes an unspecified mixture of NO and NO_2 molecules.)

Lightning strikes can fix atmospheric dinitrogen (NO_x deposition), but from common experience we know that thunderstorms in temperate regions are very sporadic, and they could never sustain the fixed nitrogen requirements of a grassland. On the other hand, clover is a very common plant, and in our ecosystem, the fixation of atmospheric dinitrogen in the roots of this plant can be considered to be the only mechanism for balancing the losses of fixed nitrogen.

Losses of fixed nitrogen are related mainly to soil nitrate, NO_3^-, which can either be leached away or converted back to dinitrogen (and N_2O or NO) through denitrification (Figure 5.6). Furthermore, ammonia may also be lost from the soil environment by volatilization. However, ammonia is a very soluble gas and it has a very short atmospheric residence time of only six days, being rapidly redeposited, either directly as the gas, or dissolved in rainwater. This is an example of ecological recycling, because there has been no net loss of fixed nitrogen on the global scale. However, the ecological recycling may be incomplete on the local scale. This is because volatilized ammonia may be consumed by atmospheric reactions (considered below), or simply blown into a nearby forest, lake, or other environment.

5.5 The biogeochemical nitrogen cycle

After that brief introduction, we shall now study the processes of the biogeochemical nitrogen cycle in detail. Again, the choice of a starting point is arbitrary, but we begin by considering the pool of organic nitrogen in the soil environment.

5.5.1 Organic nitrogen

On a global scale, organic matter is the most important reservoir of nitrogen in terrestrial ecosystems (Table 5.1). However, much of this organic matter is unavailable for biogeochemical recycling.

○ Can you think of a present-day environment that contains 'fossil' organic matter that is not being recycled?

● A peat bog is a good example. This is a highly reducing environment in which organic matter can remain largely intact.

While a peat bog may be quite unusual as an environment, one can find organic matter that is difficult to recycle in more common environments. For example, a leaf will release its nutrients far more readily than the fallen trunk of a tree. Indeed, the pool of organic nitrogen in the soil environment is highly complex, although for simplicity, we are not going to consider the soil biota (bacteria, worms, etc.) in our pool of organic nitrogen. In our case, the organic matter is assumed to consist of decaying grass, clover and rabbits, together with waste products from living rabbits. Even so, the potential range of organic compounds is vast because the organisms will be in all stages of decay, from relatively fresh to nearly totally decomposed.

However, despite this complexity, the end-point of the decomposition of organic nitrogen is simple inorganic species. Of these, NH_4^+ is the most important; it is produced from organic matter by a process known as **mineralization**.

Table 5.1 Total fixed nitrogen in soils and terrestrial biomass.

Component	Mass of nitrogen/ 10^{12} kg
soil (organic)	300
soil (inorganic)	10
biomass (plants)	10
biomass (animals)	0.2

5.5.2 Mineralization of organic nitrogen

Mineralization is a term that is not restricted to the nitrogen cycle, but can be equally applied to other biogeochemical cycles. It simply means the conversion of an organic form of an element to an inorganic form. For nitrogen, it is taken to mean the formation of NH_4^+ from organic matter.

Bacteria play an important role in the mineralization of soil organic nitrogen, although mineralization is not restricted to the soil environment, and the process also takes place within all organisms (including humans) whenever they consume proteins. Proteins are simply strings of amino acids, which consist of a carbon skeleton and an amino group.

The major steps in the complete breakdown of protein in an adult human are shown in Figure 5.7.

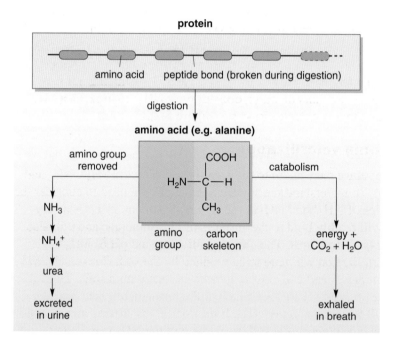

Figure 5.7 The breakdown of protein in an adult human. Dietary protein is digested to amino acids in the gut and excess amino acids are then catabolized within body cells. Catabolism is the breakdown of complex organic molecules, often involving the release of energy.

During digestion, the **peptide bonds** that link the amino acids together in an intact protein are broken, releasing the individual amino acids. (A peptide bond is simply the name given to the bond that binds two amino acids together.) A proportion of these amino acids are used by the body to make its own proteins and repair damaged tissues. However, healthy adult humans consume protein in excess of their growth and maintenance needs and the surplus amino acids are available as an energy source. The amino groups are removed and the carbon skeletons are catabolized to CO_2 and water, as shown in Figure 5.7. Although nitrogen is released initially as NH_3, this molecule is rapidly converted to NH_4^+. The two species are related by the chemical equilibrium:

$$NH_3 + H^+ \rightleftharpoons NH_4^+ \tag{5.4}$$

Furthermore, the higher the concentration of H^+, the more NH_4^+ will be the dominant species. For the biogeochemical nitrogen cycle a moderately alkaline pH value of 9.25 is an important number to remember, for reasons described below.

At pH 9.25 the concentrations of NH_4^+ and NH_3 are equal, whereas under more acid conditions, NH_4^+ is the dominant species; conversely NH_3 is the dominant species under alkaline conditions. We shall return to this pH dependency later, but for the moment we shall simply note that the cells of living organisms generally have pH values between 6 and 8; therefore NH_4^+ is the dominant species in living organisms. Because the concentration of NH_4^+ has an influence on pH, the accumulation of NH_4^+ in the bodies of organisms has toxic consequences, so organisms that are using the carbon skeleton of an amino acid as an energy source must eliminate the NH_4^+ as soon as it forms.

Most aquatic organisms can cycle unlimited amounts of water and the NH_4^+ simply dissolves and diffuses away. However, birds, reptiles and insects, which cycle only very limited amounts of water, convert NH_4^+ to uric acid. Uric acid is rather insoluble and can be precipitated and excreted in a concentrated solid form, without significant water loss. This is the reason why guano (bird-droppings) is such a good nitrogen fertilizer. However, most mammals (including humans), which cycle moderate amounts of water, convert their NH_4^+ to urea, $CO(NH_2)_2$, a soluble compound that is excreted in urine (Figure 5.7).

5.5.3 Ammonia volatilization

In this section we return once again to the equilibrium between NH_4^+, NH_3 and H^+ (Equation 5.4). To understand the significance of pH, we need to consider the chemical properties of NH_4^+ and NH_3 in the soil environment. NH_4^+ is a very 'sticky' ion that will readily bind to the surfaces of clay minerals, and will also enter into their crystal structures. Thus, in acid soils (around pH 6) NH_4^+ produced by mineralization will tend to be retained by the soil. Conversely, NH_3 does not bind to minerals and can exist in a gaseous state within soils. Thus, if the soil is alkaline (around pH 9), then much of the nitrogen released by mineralization will be in the form of NH_3. If the conditions are dry, and there is significant air movement above the soil, then much of the NH_3 may be lost (volatilized) from the soil.

However, a more general case of ammonia volatilization concerns animal wastes. In our ecosystem (Figure 5.6), the rabbits eat plant protein and excrete the waste nitrogen in the form of urea. This lies on, or close to, the surface of the soil, where it decomposes to NH_3 and CO_2. The reaction is catalysed by urease, an enzyme common to many soil microbes, which may also release urease directly into the soil, where it will bind with clay minerals. In such a case urease would be termed a soil enzyme. The basic reaction is:

$$CO(NH_2)_2 + H_2O \xrightarrow{\text{urease}} 2NH_3 + CO_2 \qquad (5.5)$$

This process may be very common on arable land, where manures and animal slurries can lose up to half of their nitrogen by ammonia volatilization. Clearly, this loss of potential soil nitrogen is costly, and much effort has been spent trying to find chemical ways to inhibit the action of urease. To date, these efforts have resulted in very limited success.

○ Can you think of a common experience that reveals the loss of soil nitrogen from animal wastes?

● Walk close to a pig farm in summer and breathe deeply through your nose. Amongst those healthy smells, you will detect NH_3.

However, although much nitrogen may be lost by volatilization, NH_3 has only a very short residence time in the atmosphere (six days), and much of the gas will be redeposited rapidly in the fields, either directly or dissolved in rainwater, although unavoidable losses of NH_3 will occur. We have noted that NH_3 may be blown away from the fields into oceans, lakes, forests and other ecosystems, but in addition, much of the volatilized NH_3 may be consumed by certain atmospheric reactions.

Human activity contributes significantly to the amount of nitrogen oxides, NO_x, and — more importantly — sulfur dioxide, SO_2, in the atmosphere, where these gases react to form nitric acid, HNO_3, and sulfuric acid, H_2SO_4. The only major basic chemical compound in the atmosphere that can neutralize these acids is the ammonia molecule, NH_3. Ammonia reacts with these acids to form fine particles of ammonium nitrate, NH_4NO_3, and ammonium sulfate, $(NH_4)_2SO_4$. There have been some suggestions that aerosols containing these molecules may have some localized effect on climate. Their high solubility in cloud and rainwater means that they will be deposited rapidly, and their contribution to global climate change is probably negligible. However, what this effect does highlight is that human interferences in biogeochemical cycles can cancel each other out, at least partially. Increasing emissions of agricultural ammonia help to neutralize increasing emissions of industrial sulfur dioxide.

5.5.4 Nitrification

Although much NH_3 may be lost through volatilization of animal wastes, mineralization of soil organic nitrogen usually leads to high levels of NH_4^+, because most soils tend to have pH values less than 7 (i.e. they are acidic). NH_4^+ is a reduced form of nitrogen and, in well oxygenated soils, nitrifying bacteria can oxidize the NH_4^+ to NO_2^- and NO_3^-, releasing energy in the process. Nitrification takes place in two sequential reactions:

$$2NH_4^+ + 3O_2 = 2NO_2^- + 2H_2O + 4H^+ \tag{5.6}$$

$$2NO_2^- + O_2 = 2NO_3^- \tag{5.7}$$

Bacteria of the genus *Nitrosomonas* are responsible for the first step, whereas *Nitrobacter* perform the second. The resulting nitrate ion, NO_3^-, is very soluble in water and can be leached from the soils, where it can lead to problems of pollution.

○ The first step of nitrification carrried out by *Nitrosomonas* (Equation 5.6) clearly removes NH_4^+ from the soil, but can you see another side-effect of this reaction?

● The reaction also produces a large amount of hydrogen ions, H^+, which will lead to a lowering of the pH, i.e. an increase in the acidity of the soil.

This increase in acidity due to nitrification can have an effect on the properties of the soil. Sustained use of ammonium-based fertilizers, and the nitrification of

NH_4^+, can affect the pH so drastically that a loss of productivity can occur. Much of this may be due to the loss of acid-sensitive organisms such as earthworms, which are vital for the maintenance of soil fertility. To combat these effects, lime (CaO) can be applied to the fields to neutralize the acidity.

5.5.5 Denitrification

This is the most important process that converts fixed nitrogen back to dinitrogen (and to N_2O and NO), and it is intimately related to the fate of dissolved nitrate. To recap, nitrate is produced during nitrification reactions in oxygen-rich environments, and can also be deposited by thunderstorms. Nitrate is highly soluble in water, highly mobile, and is also a very strong oxidizing agent.

Although nitrate may be produced in oxygen-rich environments, it may subsequently be transported into highly reducing environments that may be very rich in organic matter. These environments can be so reducing that all of the available oxygen has been consumed, yet a large amount of organic matter still remains.

A soil that is well aerated at the surface, but waterlogged at depth, is depicted in Figure 5.8. In the well-aerated soil, the supply of oxygen is not a problem, so organic nitrogen is converted to nitrate which may be used by the biota, although much will be leached from the soil. At depth, water saturation greatly reduces the diffusion of oxygen, and the potential rate of microbial oxidation is greater than the supply of oxygen. However, nitrate from the overlying aerated soil is washed into the waterlogged zone, and we have noted that nitrate is a strong oxidizing agent. Under these conditions, denitrifying bacteria, such as *Pseudomonas*, can continue to oxidize the organic matter using nitrate instead of oxygen, the end-products being N_2, N_2O and NO, which can all be returned to the atmosphere.

○ Can you think of any other environments where denitrification may occur?

● Denitrification will occur in any aquatic environment that is rich in organic matter and has a limited supply of oxygen, and into which nitrate can be added, either directly or by diffusion. For example, nitrate produced in the uppermost layers of a stagnant pond will diffuse to lower oxygen-free levels, where it will be used by denitrifying bacteria for the oxidation of organic matter. The same process occurs on a much larger scale in both lakes and the open oceans.

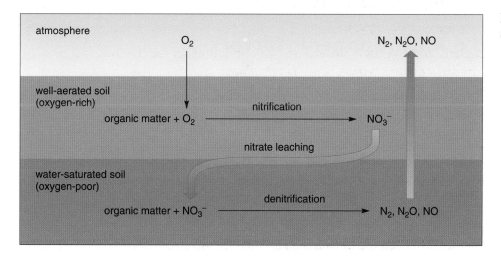

Figure 5.8 Denitrification within a waterlogged soil.

We have noted that denitrification is the principal process that converts fixed nitrogen back to atmospheric dinitrogen and that these losses of fixed nitrogen have to be balanced by nitrogen fixation (Figures 5.2 and 5.3). However, the production of nitrous oxide, N_2O, is perhaps of more concern.

Nitrous oxide is a *greenhouse gas* that is over 300 times more effective in retaining heat than carbon dioxide. Although the atmospheric concentration of nitrous oxide (0.31 ppmv) is much less than that of carbon dioxide (360 ppmv), nitrous oxide contributes about 5% of the total anthropogenic greenhouse effect. Nitrous oxide also has a very long atmospheric residence time of 170 years.

○ From what you have learned so far, can you think of one way that human activity may be leading to an increase in atmospheric nitrous oxide?

● Modern agriculture requires the use of synthetic fertilizers fixed by the Haber–Bosch process. Some of this fixed nitrogen is returned to the atmosphere by denitrification, which will increase levels of atmospheric nitrous oxide.

Although agriculture is the most important source of atmospheric nitrous oxide, other anthropogenic sources include fuel combustion and nitric acid production. Partly as a result of the long atmospheric residence time of nitrous oxide, human activity has increased the level of atmospheric nitrous oxide by 13%, from 0.275 ppmv to 0.310 ppmv.

5.5.6   Assimilation of inorganic nutrients

In the above discussion, we have shown that organic nitrogen is converted to the ammonium ion, NH_4^+, during mineralization, which is then oxidized to nitrate, NO_3^-, during nitrification in oxygen-rich soils. Once formed, nitrate may be lost by conversion to dinitrogen, nitrous oxide and nitric oxide during denitrification, or may simply be leached from the soils. However, we have already noted that the ammonium ion and the nitrate ion are both biologically active, hence they may be recycled (assimilated) by plants, and the nitrogen retained by the ecosystem. In the case of nitrate, enzymes present in the organisms, called reductases, convert the nitrate ion to the ammonium ion before the nitrogen can be used for the synthesis of amino acids.

5.6 Anthropogenic factors

So far, we have considered nitrogen fixation in some detail, the necessity of the use of fertilizers, and then looked at the ecology of a temperate grassland ecosystem, highlighting the various processes involved. Several times we have mentioned the problem of nitrate pollution, which is one of the main consequences of human activity. In the following section, we concentrate on the main causes of nitrate pollution, its effects on human beings (both physical and social) and the environment, and we consider one way in which these effects might be mitigated in the future.

5.6.1 Fertilizers and ploughing

Repeated planting and harvesting of a non-fixing plant such as wheat will eventually remove so much fixed nitrogen that the soils will lose their fertility. In order to avoid this, farmers must apply fertilizers to the fields. These fertilizers are commonly ammonium salts, ammonia solutions, nitrates, urea and animal wastes. For economic reasons, they are often applied in a single large dose, whereas natural biological fixation is a continuous process. These single large doses of fertilizers could be considered as a bonus for the soil biota, which can recycle a large proportion of the nutrients in the fertilizer before they can be assimilated by crops such as wheat. Furthermore, fields are often ploughed, which not only enhances mineralization through the dispersal of organic matter throughout the soil, but also introduces atmospheric oxygen into soils that may already be oxidizing. Thus we have enhanced mineralization, which produces large amounts of ammonium ions in an oxidizing environment where the nitrification reactions will convert ammonium to nitrate. Clearly, the net result of ploughing reduced inorganic and organic fertilizers into an oxidizing environment is the production of nitrates.

[handwritten margin note: O_2 + mineralisation => Ammonium ions. Ammonium → Nitrate]

5.6.2 Nitrate pollution

We have noted that NH_4^+ is a 'sticky' ion that tends to be retained by soils. However, NO_3^- is the most mobile form of nitrogen in most soils. Nitrates can easily move through aquifers, and find their way into rivers and lakes and will ultimately be present in drinking water. There is no economically viable means of removing nitrates from water. Two potential threats to human health have been identified, although opinions differ widely as to how real they are. The first of these is methaemoglobinaemia, or 'blue-baby' syndrome, where the supply of oxygen to the bloodstream is restricted because nitrite ions, NO_2^-, formed from ingested nitrate ions, compete with oxygen for uptake by haemoglobin. The symptoms are similar to those of carbon monoxide poisoning. The second is that nitrate ions can react with amines in the gut to form carcinogenic compounds. Because of the uncertainties surrounding the extent of the risks, the World Health Organization (WHO) recommends that levels of NO_3^- and NO_2^- in drinking water should be less than $50\,mg\,l^{-1}$ and less than $3\,mg\,l^{-1}$ respectively.

While there are uncertainties regarding the toxicity of nitrate, there can be little doubt that they can have an adverse effect on the environment. Where plant growth is limited by the supply of fixed nitrogen, the addition of nitrate will result in increased growth. In an agricultural setting, this may be exactly what is required. Where aquatic plants are limited by nitrogen supply, increased nitrate in the water can lead to an 'explosion' in the growth of plants and algae. For example, the runoff of agricultural nitrate has resulted in prodigious growth of marine algae, referred to as 'algal blooms', including toxic species, in the shallow seas around the coast of Brittany. The phenomenon is termed 'marées vertes' (green seas), and with each tide, algae are deposited on the sands, where they rot in the sunshine. In certain areas, these green and smelly sands have had adverse effects on the tourist industry, and have led to expensive clean-up operations. Similarly, surface algal blooms in a restricted environment, such as a small lake, can seriously disrupt the ecology, simply because most aquatic organisms will be deprived of sunlight. This can lead to the death of many organisms, and their decomposition will consume oxygen, resulting in stagnation.

5.6.3 Zero-tillage agricultural practices

In addition to the enhanced production of nitrates, the continued ploughing of agricultural land has also resulted in many other long-term problems such as soil erosion, a general decrease in the amount of organic matter present within the soil (enhanced mineralization), and loss of soil moisture. For all of these reasons, there has been much effort dedicated to the development of 'zero-tillage' agricultural practices, where 'ploughing in' is simply abandoned.

By definition, zero-tillage seeding is a one-step operation that places seed and fertilizer into an undisturbed seedbed, and retains sufficient stubble from the previous year's crop to prevent soil erosion and retain soil moisture. Specialized machines cut a thin 'slit' in the soil where fertilizer and seeds are deposited in precisely the right quantities, at precisely the right depth. Although not suited to all climates, the results have justified the effort and, with proper management, yields may be as good or better than those obtained with traditional techniques.

5.7 Where next for nitrogen in world agriculture?

In the above discussion we have used nitrogen as an example to examine certain aspects of the ecology of a temperate grassland. We have shown that it was necessary for humans to intervene in the 'natural order' so that they could provide sufficient food for the global population. This intervention is related mainly to the use of fertilizers, and we have considered some of the associated environmental problems. However, the world's human population continues to rise, which will obviously require increased agricultural output, and nitrogen will play a key role. The question is: how should we react in order both to prevent famine and minimize environmental problems, which themselves have implications for the welfare of people? Three possible answers are considered below.

5.7.1 Build more Haber–Bosch plants

Building more Haber–Bosch plants could be considered as a kind of 'sledge-hammer' approach, where one just continues with present practices, but simply increases the amount of nitrogen fertilizer being produced. It is already known that this is not an ideal farming practice, and that much fertilizer is lost through biogeochemical cycling, which is a waste of money, harmful to the environment, and may have implications for human health. Also, both the raw materials and energy source for the Haber–Bosch process are fossil fuels, the use of which contributes to global warming.

5.7.2 Molecular biotechnology

Molecular biotechnology or genetic engineering is an emotive subject, although there can be little doubt that great benefits have been achieved through the bacterial production of drugs such an insulin (for the treatment of diabetes) and interferons (for cancer, multiple sclerosis and hepatitis therapy, for example), but what about the biogeochemical nitrogen cycle? In the early years of molecular biotechnology there was much hope that the nitrogen-fixing capabilities of legumes could be transferred to non-fixing plants such as wheat, which would have solved all of the problems associated with fertilizers. However, subsequent research has revealed the complexity of nitrogen fixation in legumes; so many genes are involved that this biotechnological innovation is probably impossible, at least in the foreseeable future. Other possibilities include the use of bacterial fertilizers, where genetically modified nitrogen-fixing bacteria are applied directly to fields, or trying to enhance the efficiency of existing nitrogen-fixing legumes.

5.7.3 More ecologically based agricultural practices

This is something that is already happening; for example, there has been an increase in 'organic' farming where the use of chemicals is either abandoned or reduced to a minimum. Furthermore, we have already considered the development of zero-tillage agricultural practices, and although crop rotation was very common in Britain in ancient times, the technique is still practised and developed in many parts of the world.

So what is the answer? Well, in the immediate future it is likely to be a combination of all three of the above possibilities. Moving towards more ecologically based methods of agriculture, introducing genetically modified organisms that have been shown to be 'safe', and using industrially produced fertilizers where necessary. Whatever the long-term solution, it is clear that much scientific research will be required in all areas of the biogeochemical nitrogen cycle.

5.8 Global fluxes of nitrogen

To end our discussion of the nitrogen biogeochemical cycle, we return to the 'global ecosystem', simply to consider the fluxes of nitrogen between the various major reservoirs of the Earth. It must be stressed that the values given are very approximate, but you should have some idea of the amount of nitrogen being exchanged between the various reservoirs each year.

Details of the nitrogen fluxes between the atmospheric, terrestrial, oceanic and crustal rock reservoirs are shown in Figure 5.9. Note that the fluxes are expressed in 10^{12} g. (For carbon fluxes we used 10^{12} kg because of the larger amounts involved.) Use the data in Figure 5.9, together with information from elsewhere in Section 5, to answer Questions 5.2–5.9 below.

Question 5.2

What is the major loss of nitrogen to the atmosphere from terrestrial sources and under what environmental conditions does this occur?

Question 5.3

Ammonia volatilization is the next most important fixed nitrogen loss from terrestrial sources (122×10^9 kg yr^{-1}), yet most of this ammonia is eventually redeposited. Under what conditions is ammonia volatilized, and why is most of it redeposited?

Question 5.4

What is the net loss of ammonia from the land to the atmosphere indicated in Figure 5.9? If one compares the net loss of ammonia from the land with the

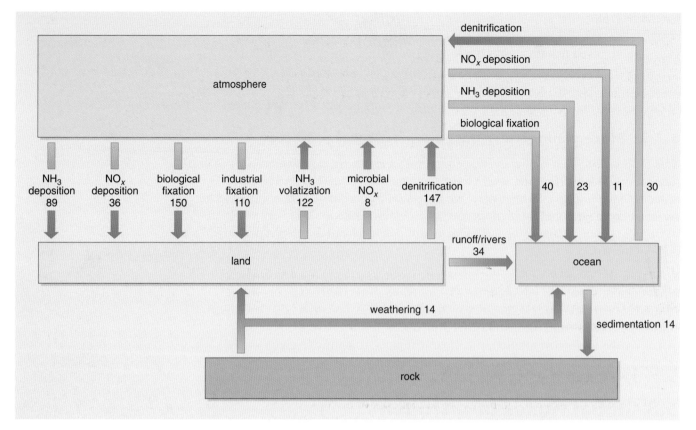

Figure 5.9 The global nitrogen cycle showing fluxes between different reservoirs. All values are quoted in units of 10^9 kg N yr^{-1}. Note that the flux of nitrogen from land to rock via sedimentation is not shown.

amount being blown out to sea, there is a discrepancy. How much ammonia disappears and where does it go?

Question 5.5

We indicated in Section 5.3.1 that thunderstorms provide about 10% of the total dinitrogen being fixed by natural processes each year. Using the data in Figure 5.9, sum the total amount of natural biological fixation (land and ocean) and sum the total amount of NO_x deposition (land and ocean). Combine the data and then express NO_x deposition as a percentage of the total non-industrially fixed nitrogen. If it exceeds 10%, then where does the additional NO_x come from?

Question 5.6

Rivers and runoff constitute a major loss of nitrogen from the land to the oceans. In what form is this nitrogen?

Question 5.7

Calculate the net input of fixed nitrogen to the oceans. If the concentration of fixed nitrogen in the oceans is increasing as a result of human activity, then what effects might this have? Is there a flux missing on Figure 5.9, relating to the oceans?

Question 5.8

Throughout Section 5 we have continually referred to losses of fixed nitrogen from soils, and Table 5.1 gives the total amount of fixed nitrogen in soils and terrestrial biomass. However, we noted that most of the soil organic nitrogen is not being recycled, so for this question, we shall assume that the amount of organic nitrogen being actively recycled is 10×10^{12} kg N yr^{-1}. From Figure 5.9 we can calculate that a total of 311×10^9 kg (0.311×10^{12} kg) of fixed nitrogen is lost from the terrestrial environments each year. What does Table 5.1 reveal about the overall efficiency of the ecological recycling of fixed nitrogen? Assuming that the yearly losses of fixed nitrogen remained constant, and that the losses of fixed nitrogen were never replenished, how long would it take for all of the fixed nitrogen to be lost from terrestrial environments?

Question 5.9

If we were to replace the rabbits in our grassland (Figure 5.6) with a dense herd of beef cattle, how might the biogeochemical nitrogen cycle of the grassland be affected? Can you think of any other adverse effects on the ecosystem? What action may be necessary to preserve the productivity of the ecosystem?

5.9 Summary of Section 5

1   The Earth's biosphere contains a constant amount of biomass that is supported by a constant level of fixed nitrogen that can be termed the 'optimum value'. During biogeochemical cycling, some of this fixed nitrogen is returned to the atmosphere as N_2 and N_2O, requiring the fixation of atmospheric N_2 to maintain the levels of fixed nitrogen at the optimum value.

2   Lightning strikes and biological nitrogen fixation are the two processes of natural N_2 fixation, although only the latter has true ecological significance, because only nitrogen-fixing organisms can respond rapidly to local needs. Industrialization, the rise of population, and political considerations led to the development of the Haber–Bosch process for the production of nitrogen-rich fertilizers.

3   In a temperate grassland ecosystem, biological nitrogen fixation, by plants such as clover, may be the only process that balances the losses of fixed nitrogen that occur through NO_3^- leaching, denitrification and NH_3 volatilization.

4   Apart from nitrogen fixation, the fundamental processes of the biogeo-chemical nitrogen cycle are: *mineralization*, where organically bound nitrogen is released into the environment as NH_4^+ (also urea and uric acid); *ammonia volatilization*, which mainly involves the breakdown of urea and the loss of NH_3; *nitrification*, where nitrifying bacteria oxidize NH_4^+ to NO_2^- and NO_3^- in oxidizing environments; *denitrification*, where denitrifying bacteria use NO_3^- instead of O_2, during the oxidation of organic matter in reducing environments; and *assimilation*, where soil NH_4^+ and NO_3^- are incorporated into plants.

5   Agricultural practices disrupt all aspects of the nitrogen cycle of a temperate grassland, enhancing the losses of fixed nitrogen, and fertilizers may have to be used to maintain the fertility of the soil. Biogeochemical cycling of fertilizers in the soil leads to significant losses of fertilizer nitrogen, which can result in the pollution of the atmosphere and aquatic environments.

Learning outcomes for Section 5

After working through this section you should be able to:

5.1 Name the Earth's major reservoirs of nitrogen. (*Questions 5.7 and 5.8*)

5.2 Describe how nitrogen is transferred between its reservoirs. (*Questions 5.2 and 5.8*)

5.3 Outline how nitrogen is fixed in nature. (*Question 5.1*)

5.4 Describe how nitrogen is fixed by humans. (*Question 5.7*)

5.5 Summarize the processes of ammonia volatilization, nitrification and denitrification. (*Questions 5.2–5.4*)

5.6 Explain the influence of agriculture on the nitrogen cycle. (*Questions 5.7 and 5.9*)

The sulfur and phosphorus cycles

6

6.1 The global sulfur cycle

Globally, the amount of sulfur in the biosphere is relatively small. Figure 6.1 shows a simple representation of the various reservoirs and fluxes of sulfur in the global sulfur cycle. Note that the various reservoirs and fluxes are in 10^{12} g and 10^{12} g yr^{-1}. (For carbon and nitrogen reservoirs we used 10^{12} kg and for carbon fluxes we used 10^{12} kg yr^{-1}, to reflect the larger amounts involved.)

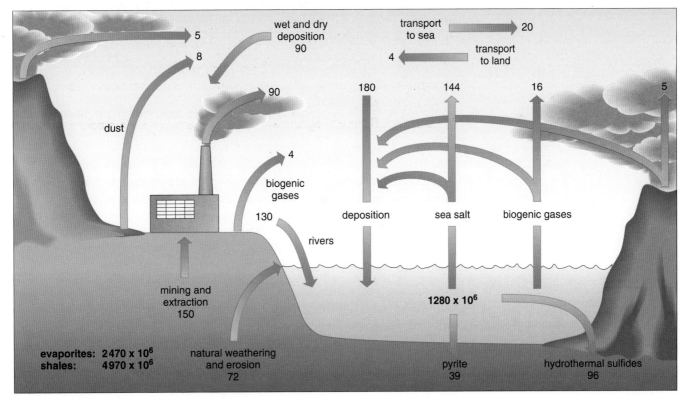

Figure 6.1   The present-day global sulfur cycle. All reservoirs (bold values) are expressed in units of 10^{12} g S and annual fluxes in units of 10^{12} g S yr^{-1}.

○ Compare Figure 6.1 with similar diagrams you have met for carbon and nitrogen. Do you think the sulfur cycle has more similarities to the carbon or nitrogen cycle?

● Both carbon and sulfur cycles are dominated by large sedimentary reservoirs. The nitrogen cycle is dominated by a large atmospheric reservoir.

The major reservoirs of sulfur on the Earth are rocks and seawater. Specifically, shales are rocks that contain the mineral pyrite, FeS_2 (Figure 6.2), in addition to sulfur-containing fossil organic matter. **Evaporite** deposits are rocks created by the evaporation of seawater (e.g. $CaSO_4$). Together, rocks and seawater account for over 99.99% of the Earth's sulfur.

Figure 6.2   The mineral pyrite (FeS_2), a major reservoir of the Earth's sulfur.

Although the main reservoirs of sulfur are in the Earth's crust, the most rapid transfers, i.e. the greatest fluxes, occur between the atmosphere, biosphere and hydrosphere. These fluxes are quantified in Figure 6.1. Reduced sulfur in the Earth's crust can be released by natural weathering and erosion (72×10^{12} g S yr^{-1}) to produce sulfate, SO_4^{2-}, upon contact with the air. For example, the following equation shows how pyrite is weathered to give sulfate:

$$4FeS_2 + 8H_2O + 15O_2 = 2Fe_2O_3 + 16H^+ + 8SO_4^{2-} \tag{6.1}$$

Sulfate can be directly assimilated by plants and microbes and is involved in the synthesis of reduced organic compounds. Animals consume these organisms and the reduced organic sulfur contained within them. When tissues die and decompose, some sulfur enters the cells of microbes, but some is released as sulfate again. There is a continuous loss of sulfur to rivers and streams, which eventually lead into the ocean.

○ Study Figure 6.1 to determine how else sulfur is transported to the ocean by natural processes.

● Some sulfur enters the ocean as atmospheric fallout, having originated from volcanic emissions.

En route to the ocean, sulfate may be reduced to H_2S or elemental sulfur by sulfate-reducing bacteria. These organisms are present in oxygen-poor environments in lakes, marshes and tidal flats and H_2S is the main sulfur-containing gas released by biological activity on land:

$$2H^+ + SO_4^{2-} + 2[CH_2O] = 2CO_2 + H_2S + 2H_2O \tag{6.2}$$

(*Note*: [CH_2O] denotes carbohydrate.)

In the oceans, sulfur is abundant and is found as sulfate. A sulfur atom present as oceanic sulfate has a residence time of around 50 million years. Rivers (130×10^{12} g S yr^{-1}) and atmospheric deposition (180×10^{12} g S yr^{-1}) provide the major inputs of sulfur to the ocean, although most atmospheric deposition of sulfur is simply sea salt returning to the sea. Sulfate is consumed by marine organisms and marine algae produce the gas dimethyl sulfide, $(CH_3)_2S$, which represents the largest natural flux of a sulfur gas to the atmosphere ($> 15 \times 10^{12}$ g S yr^{-1}). Once in the atmosphere, dimethyl sulfide forms methylsulfonic acid, CH_3SO_3H, and sulfur dioxide, SO_2, which act as condensation nuclei for water vapour and therefore produce clouds. This process is important for the Earth's climate as increased cloud cover raises the Earth's albedo, so more solar radiation is reflected back into space. Stated simply, the more algae there are in the ocean, the cooler the Earth may become. Records in Greenland and Antarctic ice show a correlation between increased concentrations of sulfur compounds and glacial periods. Dimethyl sulfide is also a natural source of acid rain because it is oxidized to sulfuric acid by reactions with hydroxyl radicals.

The largest flux of sulfur out of the ocean is the precipitation of metallic sulfides at hydrothermal vents (96×10^{12} g S yr^{-1}). The second largest output is the production of biogenic pyrite in marine sediments (39×10^{12} g S yr^{-1}). Pyrite is formed in oxygen-poor conditions such as are found in sediments under areas of high marine productivity. The decomposing remains of the marine organisms exhaust the oxygen supply in the sediments, forcing microbes to use sulfate as an oxidizing agent:

$$2[CH_2O] + SO_4^{2-} = S^{2-} + 2CO_2 + 2H_2O \qquad (6.3)$$

The sulfide (S^{2-}) then combines with iron to produce pyrite (FeS_2).

The proportion of organic sulfur in the marine sediments is relatively small because most of it undergoes biological transformation to sulfide and then pyrite. Sulfur can also be removed by the formation of evaporite rocks. If a basin becomes isolated from the open ocean, evaporation concentrates minerals such as gypsum, $CaSO_4.2H_2O$:

$$Ca^{2+} + SO_4^{2-} + 2H_2O = CaSO_4.2H_2O \qquad (6.4)$$

The sulfur in sediments is locked up until these sediments are uplifted and exposed to weathering by tectonic activity and, on average, a sulfur atom will spend around 260 million years in sedimentary rocks.

○ Study Figure 6.1 and suggest how human activities may affect fluxes of sulfur from the crust.

● Human extraction and mining have accelerated the movement of sulfur from the crust.

Question 6.1

Which natural atmospheric process do you think has been exacerbated by the anthropogenically increased flux of sulfur from the crust to the atmosphere? (You may be aware of some of the problems this causes from frequent media reports.)

6.2 The global phosphorus cycle

Figure 6.3 is a simple representation of the global phosphorus cycle. Comparing the various reservoir sizes clearly shows that the majority of the Earth's phosphorus is locked up in the crust. In fact, crustal phosphorus is mostly in the mineral apatite, $Ca_5(PO_4)_3OH$ (Figure 6.4). Only a tiny fraction of the crust is phosphorus-rich but all rocks contain at least a trace amount. The phosphorus content of the crust is massive in relation to the combined marine and terrestrial inorganic and organic pools.

Figure 6.3 The present-day global phosphorus cycle. All reservoirs (bold values) are expressed in units of 10^{12} g P and annual fluxes in units of 10^{12} g P yr^{-1}.

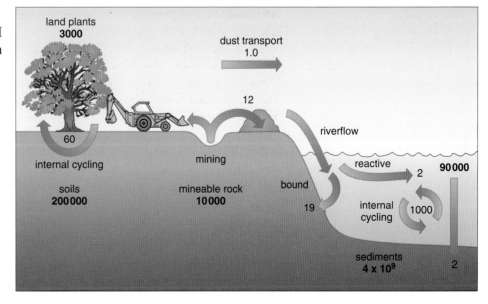

land plants
3000

dust transport
1.0

12

riverflow

60

internal cycling

mining

reactive

2

90 000

soils
200 000

mineable rock
10 000

bound

internal
cycling

1000

19

sediments
4 x 10⁹

2

Figure 6.4   Apatite, $Ca_5(PO_4)_3OH$, the mineral in which the majority of the Earth's phosphorus is present.

○   Look again at the phosphorus cycle displayed in Figure 6.3 and compare it with the carbon, nitrogen and sulfur cycles you met earlier. What makes the phosphorus cycle different from the other cycles?

●   Phosphorus has no gaseous reservoir.

The atmospheric component of the phosphorous cycle is extremely small and comprises material introduced as wind-blown dust particles. This material is returned to the Earth's surface by settling as dry particles. Phosphorus does, however, naturally form a gas called phosphine (PH_3) but it is restricted to very specialized local conditions.

○   By considering the chemical formula of phosphine, what sort of environment would it be present in?

●   Phosphine is a reduced gas and hence it is restricted to oxygen-poor reducing environments such as saltmarshes.

The main fluxes between the various phosphorus reservoirs are noted on Figure 6.3. To aid our understanding of the phosphorus cycle, let us follow a phosphorus atom through the cycle. We will begin on land where almost all the phosphorus is derived from weathering reactions that release the phosphorus from apatite as soluble phosphate:

$$Ca_5(PO_4)_3OH + 4H_2CO_3 = 5Ca^{2+} + 3HPO_4^{2-} + 4HCO_3^- + H_2O \qquad (6.5)$$

Phosphate is a form of phosphorus that can be assimilated by organisms. However, most phosphate reacts with soil minerals such as iron and aluminium oxides and becomes unassimilable. Decomposing organic matter returns organic forms of phosphorus to the water and soil and this once again may be utilized by organisms. The phosphorus content of most rocks and soils is relatively small and organisms rely on rapid phosphorus recycling for survival. In the terrestrial ecosystem, the flux of phosphorus between the soil and biota is almost a closed system and $60 \times 10^{12}\,g\,P\,yr^{-1}$ is rapidly recycled in this way (Figure 6.3). Most of the phosphate only breaks free of the terrestrial phosphorus cycle when soil erosion allows solid particles to be transported by running water.

The flux of phosphorus carried in rivers is $21 \times 10^{12}\,g\,P\,yr^{-1}$. The majority of this ($19 \times 10^{12}\,g\,P\,yr^{-1}$) is adsorbed to iron and aluminium oxides that are carried as suspended particles and buried in river sediments on the continental shelf. The remainder ($2 \times 10^{12}\,g\,P\,yr^{-1}$) enters the ocean as dissolved phosphate and is assimilable by marine organisms. Additional phosphorus is added to the oceans as wind-blown dust.

Most of the dissolved phosphorus that is added to the oceans from rivers is fixed by marine organisms. The turnover of phosphorus in the surface ocean occurs in a few days and 90% of this element taken up by marine organisms is regenerated in the surface ocean. The remainder is steadily lost through the water column, generating a concentration of phosphorus in the deep ocean that is much greater than that in the surface ocean (not indicated on Figure 6.3).

In some parts of the world, the phosphorus-rich waters of the deep ocean can upwell and re-introduce phosphorus to surface waters. This stimulates the growth of phytoplankton, so regions of upwelling tend to be associated with high levels of primary production. For example, upwelling off the coast of Peru supports economically important anchovy fisheries.

The residence time for oceanic phosphorus is 25 000 years and each phosphorus atom may complete 50 cycles between the surface and deep ocean before being buried. About $2.0 \times 10^{12} \, g \, P \, yr^{-1}$ is buried in marine sediments.

○ As there are no significant gaseous losses of phosphorus from the oceans, outputs of phosphorus are restricted to the $2.0 \times 10^{12} \, g \, P \, yr^{-1}$ buried in marine sediments. Examine Figure 6.3 and suggest how this output is replenished.

● The outputs of phosphorus to marine sediments are balanced by the inputs of dissolved phosphorus from rivers.

Once ocean-floor sediments are buried and lithified, the phosphorus is again locked up in sedimentary rock until that rock is exhumed and weathering can commence again. Perhaps more than any other biogeochemical cycle we have examined, the phosphorus cycle is reliant on tectonic activity to facilitate recycling.

In common with many other biogeochemical cycles, human activities have disturbed the natural phosphorus cycle. Around $12 \times 10^{12} \, g \, P \, yr^{-1}$ is released from the geosphere by mining, most of which goes to the production of phosphate fertilizers. The phosphorus incorporated into agricultural crops from fertilizers is removed through harvesting and is eventually released as human or animal sewage. Sewage treatment removes around 40% of this phosphorus but the remainder finds its way into rivers, lakes and the sea.

Question 6.2

Phosphorous can be a limiting nutrient in ecosystems and, as a result, phosphate fertilizers are commonly used in agriculture. However, too much phosphorus can be toxic. Considering that (a) phosphate binds with oxides of iron and aluminium in soil and (b) due to soil erosion, these compounds often enter lakes and rivers, where the phosphate may be released back into solution, suggest potential drawbacks to the excessive use on agricultural land of phosphate fertilizers. (*Hint*: remember from Section 6.1 that decomposing organic remains can remove oxygen.)

Question 6.3

Examine the sizes of the reservoirs in the global sulfur and phosphorus cycles and suggest what these two cycles have in common.

Question 6.4

Look again at the fluxes from the ocean in the various biogeochemical cycles. In what way is the phosphorus cycle different from the carbon, nitrogen and sulfur cycles?

6.3 Summary of Section 6

1   Most of the sulfur in the sulfur cycle is present in the crust.

2   Minerals containing reduced sulfur are weathered to sulfate.

3   H_2S is the major biogenic gas produced on land, while dimethyl sulfide, $(CH_3)_2S$, is the major biogenic gas produced in the ocean.

4   $(CH_3)_2S$ can have a significant effect on the Earth's climate.

5   The major fluxes out of the ocean are the precipitation of hydrothermal minerals and the production of biogenic pyrite.

6   Most of the Earth's phosphorus is present in the crust as the mineral apatite.

7   Unlike the carbon, nitrogen and sulfur cycles, the phosphorus cycle has no gaseous reservoir.

8   Phosphorus is scarce in most environments and has to be rapidly recycled by organisms.

9   In the ocean, phosphorus lost to marine sediments is replenished by dissolved phosphate from rivers.

Learning outcomes for Section 6

After working through this section you should be able to:

6.1 Name the Earth's major reservoirs of sulfur. (*Question 6.3*)

6.2 Describe how sulfur is transferred between its reservoirs. (*Question 6.4*)

6.3 Name the Earth's major reservoirs of phosphorus. (*Question 6.3*)

6.4 Outline the main differences between the phosphorus cycle and the carbon, nitrogen and sulfur cycles. (*Question 6.4*)

6.5 Describe how phosphorus is transferred between its reservoirs. (*Question 6.4*)

6.6 Give examples of the ways in which human activity affects the sulfur and phosphorus cycles. (*Questions 6.1 and 6.2*)

The Earth system

7

7.1 Modelling the Earth system

In the early 1980s, attempts were being made to interpret the biogeochemical processes of the Earth's surface environments within a framework of cycles. Prompted by this, Robert Garrels and Abraham Lerman developed a model that consisted of a system of sedimentary reservoirs, which reflected different compartments of the environment and the fluxes that transported material between them (Figure 7.1). The Garrels and Lerman model perfectly illustrates the interactions within and between the biogeochemical cycles.

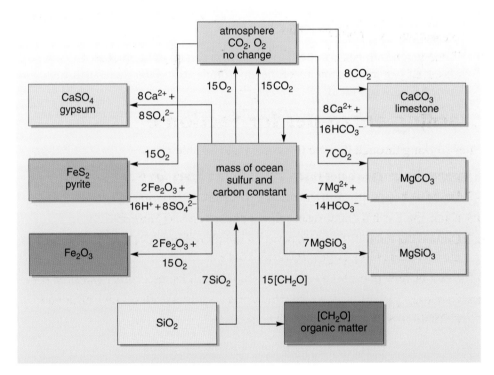

Figure 7.1 The Garrels and Lerman model, which reflects the biogeochemistry of the Earth's surface.

To run the model, we will assume there is no change in the atmospheric levels of CO_2 or O_2 and no change in the mass of carbon and sulfur in the ocean.

- First, we will increase the amount of organic matter (represented in shorthand by $[CH_2O]$) in marine sediments by 15 moles. This sets in motion a series of events:

- With no change in the CO_2 content of the atmosphere or ocean, the carbon we have added must be derived from the weathering of carbonate minerals on land ($CaCO_3$ and $MgCO_3$ boxes).

- Weathering of carbonate minerals would also transport Ca and Mg to the oceans. To maintain a constant seawater chemistry, the Ca must be removed by forming $CaSO_4$ and the Mg must be removed by forming $MgSiO_3$.

- To deposit $CaSO_4$ with no change in the SO_4^{2-} content of the ocean, sulfur must be drawn from another pool, so oxidation of pyrite (FeS_2) provides SO_4^{2-} to the ocean, whilst consuming some of the oxygen released by photosynthesis and organic matter burial. The remaining oxygen would be combined with Fe to produce Fe_2O_3.

It is clear then that in the biogeochemical system, nothing happens in isolation. Each reaction has far-reaching consequences. Garells and Lerman compared their model of the Earth's biogeochemical system to a collection of water-containing aquaria, linked by pipes, and mounted in the hold of a ship. Water would move among the aquaria as the ship pitched and rolled on the high sea, but the total mass of the reservoirs would remain the same. Furthermore, if a storm set in, some aquaria may, temporarily, hold large amounts of water, but once the storm had abated the water levels in the aquaria would return to some average value. It is interesting to reflect on the various biogeochemical cycles we have studied and consider the various residence times of the elements. Then we can begin to imagine just how long the 'storm damage' of anthropogenic activity will persist for our Earth system.

7.2 Summary of Section 7

1   The biogeochemistry of the Earth's surface can be thought of as a system of reservoirs, or compartments of the environment, and the fluxes that transport material between them.

2   The Garrels and Lerman model illustrates the interconnected nature of the Earth system.

Learning outcome for Section 7

After working through this section you should be able to:

7.1 Consider the consequences of the transfer of material from one biogeochemical reservoir to another.

Answers to questions

cycle. The Earth's tonic cycle, causes ft of mountains. ion and the hrough the

gas (which may be xide or nitrogen oxides) the atmosphere and

ange of elements at mid-eanic lithosphere onto continents at convergent plate margins; igneous activity at convergent plate margins, including both magma and volcanic gases.

(b) Surface to interior: subduction of part of the ocean-floor sediments at convergent plate margins.

Question 2.4

Using Equation 2.1:

With the Na data,

$$\text{weathering rate} = \frac{4.6 \text{ kg ha}^{-1} \text{ yr}^{-1}}{(0.016 - 0.010) \text{ kg kg}^{-1}}$$

$$= 770 \text{ kg ha}^{-1} \text{ yr}^{-1}$$

With the K data,

$$\text{weathering rate} = \frac{0.1 \text{ kg ha}^{-1} \text{ yr}^{-1}}{(0.029 - 0.024) \text{ kg kg}^{-1}}$$

$$= 20 \text{ kg ha}^{-1} \text{ yr}^{-1}$$

With the Mg data,

$$\text{weathering rate} = \frac{1.8 \text{ kg ha}^{-1} \text{ yr}^{-1}}{(0.011 - 0.001) \text{ kg kg}^{-1}}$$

$$= 180 \text{ kg ha}^{-1} \text{ yr}^{-1}$$

Question 2.5

(a) The following list summarizes processes within the rock cycle that influence the atmosphere, as well as aspects of the atmosphere that influence the rock cycle.

- Gases are added to the atmosphere from volcanoes.
- Winds, rain and ice cause weathering and/or transport of sedimentary material.
- Desert sediments are mostly transported in, and deposited from, air.
- Rock-forming organisms such as corals (forming certain limestones) and plants (forming coal and chalk) influence the atmosphere's composition through photosynthesis and respiration.

(b) The only way for an atom to escape from the mantle is by getting incorporated into a magma that then rises towards the surface. Thereafter, the magma could form a volcanic rock on the surface. If this undergoes weathering and erosion, then it can become a sedimentary rock. Alternatively, if the magma solidifies underground, as an intrusive igneous rock, then it will have to be uplifted and exposed by erosion before the process of forming a sedimentary rock can proceed. Other alternatives are that the intrusive rock could be metamorphosed before being exposed at the surface and eroded, or the metamorphic rock could be melted to produce another magma, which could then embark on any of the previous paths before ending up as a sedimentary rock. A further possibility is if the atom in question was erupted as part of a volcanic gas. Atoms like carbon, oxygen or sulfur could then end up in a chemical precipitate or in biological material that becomes incorporated into sediment. (The pathways will depend on the nature of the particular atom.)

Question 3.1

If the Earth's finite amount of the biogenic elements could no longer be recycled, they would eventually become exhausted and life would cease.

Question 3.2

The term 'biogeochemical' tells you that both the biosphere and the geosphere are involved.

Question 4.1

The flux of carbon deposited in soil is 60×10^{12} kg C yr^{-1} and at any one time the amount in the reservoir is 1500×10^{12} kg C. The mean residence time for carbon in soil is therefore $(1500 \times 10^{12}$ kg C$)/(60 \times 10^{12}$ kg C yr$^{-1}) = 25$ years.

Question 4.2

(a) The long-term record of atmospheric CO_2 levels at Mauna Loa indicates that CO_2 concentrations are steadily increasing. (b) Atmospheric CO_2 levels have risen by over 45 ppmv between 1958 and 1998.

Question 4.3

Increased CO_2 concentrations in the atmosphere would lead to a corresponding increase of dissolved CO_2 in the ocean. Because dissolved CO_2 forms an acidic solution, the average acidity of the ocean would increase and the carbonate compensation depth would shift to a shallower level. The area of carbonate sediments in Figure 4.5 would decrease.

Question 4.4

Because the oxidation product of CH_4 is CO_2, which is another greenhouse gas, the carbon atoms continue to play a role in greenhouse warming after CH_4 is destroyed.

Question 4.5

Atmospheric oxygen levels would increase. For each carbon atom that enters the rock reservoir, one oxygen molecule is left behind in the atmosphere.

Question 5.1

Thunderstorms are entirely random processes that will deposit fixed nitrogen on ecosystems irrespective of whether it will be used or not. For example, a thunderstorm could deposit fixed nitrogen on a lake that was already heavily polluted with nitrates, which would simply exacerbate an existing ecological problem.

Question 5.2

Soil nitrogen is lost mainly by denitrification, which occurs in environments that contain a limited supply of molecular oxygen and a large proportion of organic matter. Denitrifying bacteria use nitrate as the oxidant,

converting fixed nitrogen back to dinitrogen and small amounts of nitrous and nitric oxides (N_2O and NO).

Question 5.3

Ammonia is volatilized from dry alkaline soils, but most importantly from animal wastes and urea-based fertilizers. It is rapidly redeposited. Ammonia is very soluble, so readily dissolves in cloud and rainwater. Its atmospheric residence time of only six days means that most of it is redeposited.

Question 5.4

Ammonia is lost from the land to the atmosphere at a rate of 122×10^9 kg N yr^{-1} and redeposited at a rate of 89×10^9 kg N yr^{-1}; thus the net ammonia loss is 33×10^9 kg N yr^{-1}. Of this 33×10^9 kg N yr^{-1}, 23×10^9 kg N yr^{-1} are blown out to sea, so 10×10^9 kg N yr^{-1} ammonia have apparently disappeared. This ammonia has been consumed during atmospheric reactions with nitric, HNO_3, and sulfuric, H_2SO_4, acids to form aerosols of ammonium nitrate, NH_4NO_3, and ammonium sulfate, $(NH_4)_2SO_4$, respectively, which are rapidly deposited on both the land and sea.

Question 5.5

The total amount of biological nitrogen fixation on land (150) and sea (40) is 190×10^9 kg N yr^{-1}. The total amount of NO_x deposition on land (36) and sea (11) is 47×10^9 kg N yr^{-1}. Adding the two together gives us 237×10^9 kg N yr^{-1}. Thus the proportion of NO_x fixed nitrogen relative to the total is

$(47 \times 10^9$ kg N yr$^{-1})/(237 \times 10^9$ kg N yr$^{-1}) = 0.198$ or 19.8%.

So the contribution of NO_x deposition to the total amount of natural nitrogen fixation is about twice what we believe to be produced from lightning processes. The additional NO_x comes from human activities, such as from the internal combustion engines of motor vehicles.

Question 5.6

Rivers may contain several different nitrogen-containing components, such as the ions NH_4^+ and NO_3^-, particulate organic matter and plant and animal debris.

Question 5.7

Total inputs of fixed nitrogen ($\times 10^9$ kg N yr^{-1}) to the ocean are from biological fixation (40), rivers/runoff

(34), ammonia deposition (23), NO_x deposition (11), and the weathering of ancient sedimentary rock (14), which when added together give 122×10^9 kg N yr^{-1}. Nitrogen outputs are by sedimentation (14) and denitrification (30), which when added together give 44×10^9 kg N yr^{-1}. Thus Figure 5.9 suggests that the concentration of nitrogen in the oceans is increasing by 78×10^9 kg N yr^{-1}, and locally this can have an effect on the environment, such as the promotion of growth of algal blooms around the Brittany coast.

Something is missing from Figure 5.9. Humans exploit the oceans as 'hunter-gatherers'. We simply harvest the oceans for fish, without putting anything back; apart from the imposition of fishing quotas, there is no real planning as one would find on a farm. So is fertilizing the oceans with additional nitrogen such a bad thing? Locally, yes, but this could again be a case of one ecological effect of human activity partially cancelling out another one.

Question 5.8

To answer this question, you simply sum the masses of the recyclable fixed nitrogen in the various components of terrestrial ecosystems (Table 5.1), and express the amount of fixed nitrogen being lost each year as a proportion of the total:

$(0.311 \times 10^{12}$ kg N $yr^{-1})/(30.2 \times 10^{12}$ kg N $yr^{-1}) = 0.01 = 1\%$

This simple calculation suggests that the losses of fixed nitrogen are very small compared to the total, and that ecological recycling is very efficient. In order to find out how long it would take for the losses of fixed nitrogen to totally deplete the terrestrial stock, we divide the total recyclable fixed nitrogen by the yearly loss, making the assumption (which may not be justified) that yearly loss is constant:

$(30.2 \times 10^{12}$ kg N$)/(0.311 \times 10^{12}$ kg N $yr^{-1}) = 97$ years

For a biogeochemical cycle, this is an extremely short period of time, reflecting that nitrogen is cycled very rapidly on a geological time-scale. Higher plants have been on the continents for a least 400 million years, so we can be fairly sure that bacteria have been very active during that time period.

Question 5.9

If we replace the rabbits with beef cattle, then losses of fixed nitrogen will occur directly through the

'harvesting' of animal protein for consumption, and the presence of the herd will lead to further losses of fixed nitrogen, due to the production and cycling of urea. Nitrogen contained in urea may be lost directly through ammonia volatilization, or oxidized to nitrate and lost through leaching and denitrification. Cattle grazing may also lead to the compaction of soils, and the trampling of new shoots of grass. The magnitude of the effects will be directly related to the density of the herd, and it is well known how many cattle a given field will be able to support. If nitrogen losses were significantly greater than replenishments by natural fixation, then fertilizers would have to be used.

Question 6.1

The production of acid rain by the reaction of atmospheric water with the sulfur-containing gases generated by volcanoes and marine organisms has been increased by the burning of fossil fuels and the release of crustal sulfur. Acid rain causes lakes and rivers to become acidic, killing off fish and other organisms. It also damages trees and buildings.

Question 6.2

(a) Phosphate that is applied to soil in the form of fertilizer becomes bound to soil particles and then is not leached through the soil into the groundwater. This property can allow phosphorus to build up to very high and even toxic levels in the soil. (b) Runoff from agricultural land, which carries sediment into watercourses, introduces extra phosphorus into rivers and lakes, where it may become released into solution. As the productivity of many aquatic ecosystems is limited by phosphorus availability, an influx of phosphorus often results in a large increase in net primary production, which in turn depletes the water body of its oxygen as the organic matter begins to decay. This oxygen depletion can result in the death of fish and other aquatic animals.

Question 6.3

In both the sulfur and phosphorus cycles, the largest reservoir of the element occurs in the geosphere.

Question 6.4

Unlike the carbon, nitrogen and sulfur cycles, in which the element is lost from the ocean in a gaseous form, the phosphorus cycle has no significant flux of phosphorus-containing gas from the ocean.

Acknowledgements for Part 2 *Cycles*

Grateful acknowledgement is made to the following sources for permission to reproduce material in this book:

Figures

Figure 2.3: Nancy Sefton/Science Photo Library; *Figure 2.4*: Skinner, B. J. and Porter, S. C. (2000) *The Dynamic Earth: An Introduction to Physical Geology*, 4th edn, John Wiley & Sons, Ltd.; *Figure 2.5*: Dave Rothery, Open University; *Figure 2.7*: Millman, J. D. and Meade, R. H. (1983) 'World-wide delivery of river sediment to the oceans', *Journal of Geology*, **91**, pp.1–21, University of Chicago Press; *Figures 4.1, 4.16, 4.18a and b*: Schimel, D. S. *et al.* (1995) 'CO$_2$ and the carbon cycle', pp. 35–71, in J. T. Houghton, L. G. Meira Filho *et al. Climate Change, 1994*, Intergovernmental Panel on Climate Change, Secretariat, c/o World Meteorological Organization; *Figure 4.3a*: Neil Sullivan/NOAA; *Figure 4.3b*: Jeremy Young, Natural History Museum; *Figure 4.3c*: Andrew Syred/Science Photo Library; *Figure 4.3d*: Derek Walton; *Figure 4.5*: Broecker, W. S. and Peng, T. H. (1982) *Tracers in the Sea*, New York: Eldgigio Press, Columbia University, p. 59, Lamont–Dohery Earth Observatory; *Figure 4.7*: Takahasti, T. (1989) *Oceanus*, **32**, pp. 22–29, Woods Hole Oceanographic Institute; *Figure 4.9*: Geoscience Features Picture Library; *Figure 4.10*: Geophotos; *Figure 4.13*: Mauna Loa Observatory, Climate Monitoring and Diagnostics Laboratory, National Oceanic and Atmospheric Administration; *Figure 4.14*: Keeling, C. D. and Whorf, T. P. (2001) 'Atmospheric CO$_2$ records from sites in the SIO air sampling network', in *Trends: A Compendium of Data on Global Change*, Carbon Dioxide Information Analysis Center, Oak Ridge National Laboratory, US Department of Energy, Oak Ridge, Tenn., USA; *Figure 4.15*: Rob Mulvaney, British Antarctic Survey; *Figures 5.1, 6.1*: Schlesinger, W. H. (ed.) (1997) 'Global Cycles', in *Biogeochemistry and Analysis of Global Change*, 2nd edn, Academic Press, London; *Figure 5.4*: Andrew Syred/Science Photo Library; *Figure 5.5*: Mike Dodd, Open University; *Figure 6.2*: Andy Tindle, Open University; *Figure 6.3*: Jahnke, R. A. (1992) in *Global Biogeochemical Cycles*, Academic Press, London; *Figure 7.1*: Garrels, R. M. and Lerman, A. (1981) 'Phanerozoic cycles of sedimentary carbon and sulfur', *Proceedings of the National Academy of Sciences, USA*, **78**, pp. 4652–4656, Dept. of Geological Sciences, Northwestern University.

Tables

Table 2.1: Reprinted from *Geochimica et Cosmochimica Acta*, **32**, pp. 531–545, Johnson, N. M. *et al.* 'Rate of chemical weathering of silicate minerals in New Hampshire', copyright © (1968) with permission from Elsevier Science; *Table 2.2*: Lewis, W. M. *et al.* (1987) 'Major element chemistry…, *Biogeochemistry*, **4**, pp.159–181, Kluwer Academic Publishers, B. V.; *Table 2.3*: Garrels, R. M. and MacKenzie, F. T. (1971) 'Evolution of sedimentary rocks', © Garrels and MacKenzie. Millman, J. D. and Meade, R. H. (1983) 'World-wide delivery of river sediment to the oceans', *Journal of Geology*, **91**, pp.1–21, University of Chicago Press; *Table 3.1*: Peter Francis, Open University.

Every effort has been made to trace all the copyright owners, but if any has been inadvertently overlooked, the publishers will be pleased to make the necessary arrangements at the first opportunity.

Index

Note: Entries in **bold** are key terms. Page numbers referring to information that is given only in a figure or caption are printed in *italics*.